MUSIC FOR LIVING

Book Three

Now and Long Ago

JAMES L. MURSELL

GLADYS TIPTON

BEATRICE LANDECK

HARRIET NORDHOLM

ROY E. FREEBURG

JACK M. WATSON

Illustrated by

FEODOR ROJANKOVSKY

SILVER BURDETT COMPANY

Morristown, N. J.

Park Ridge, Ill.   Palo Alto   Dallas   Atlanta

Acknowledgments

We are indebted to the following for use of material in this book. If careful research has not uncovered all copyright owners, please forgive us.

University of Alabama Press, for "Clear the Line" from FOLK SONGS OF ALABAMA by Byron Arnold.

Edward Deming Andrews, for "Mince Pie or Pudding" from his book THE GIFT TO BE SIMPLE, SONGS, DANCES AND RITUALS, copyright by Edward Deming Andrews, New York 1940.

Artists and Writers Guild, Inc., for the poem "Wind in the Corn" from WONDERFUL STORY BOOK by Margaret Wise Brown.

M. Baron & Co., for "Tinga Layo" from CALYPSO SONGS OF THE WEST INDIES.

Bayley & Ferguson Ltd., for "Tam o' the Linn" from MIN-STRELSY OF CHILDHOOD by Frank Kidson and Alfred Moffatt.

Harry Behn for his poem "Halloween" from THE LITTLE HILL, published by Harcourt, Brace and Company, Inc., copyright 1949 by Harry Behn.

Boosey and Hawkes, Inc., for "A Churning Lilt" from SONGS OF THE HEBRIDES by D. Kennedy-Fraser. Copyright 1921 by Boosey and Co. Renewed 1948. Used by permission.

B. A. Botkin, for "Sandy Land" from AMERICAN PLAY-PARTY TUNES OF OKLAHOMA, by B. A. Botkin.

Paul Burlin, for the poem "Laguna Corn Grinding Song" translated by Natalie Curtis, from THE INDIANS' BOOK.

Carib Singers, for "Hi-dee-roon."

Cooperative Recreation Service, Inc., for "My Twenty Pennies" from AMIGOS CANTANDO by Olcutt and Phyllis Sanders, and for "Calling the Cows" from SWISS ALPINE SONGS.

The Devin-Adair Co., for "Moon Cradle" ("The Ballad of Downal Baun") by Padraic Colum, from THE COLLECTED POEMS OF PADRAIC COLUM.

Dodd, Mead & Co., Inc., for "Lullaby" ("Naked Bear") and "Mosquito Buzzing" from AMERICAN PRIMITIVE MUSIC by Frederick Burton.

E. P. Dutton & Co., Inc., for the poem "In the Fashion" from WHEN WE WERE VERY YOUNG by A. A. Milne; for "Louisiana Lullaby" from SING IT YOURSELF by Dorothy Gordon. E. P. Dutton & Co., Inc., and Rupert Crew Ltd., London, for the poem "Swing High" ("The Swing") from HONEY FOR TEA (NURS-ERY VERSERY) by Patience Strong. Published 1950 by E. P. Dutton & Co., Inc., and reprinted by permission of the publisher.

Mary O. Eddy, for "There Was a Man and He Was Mad" from her book BALLADS AND SONGS FROM OHIO, published by J. J. Augustin, Inc.

Editions Familiales de France, Paris, for "Walking down the Roadway" ("Je vais ou va la route") from CHANSONS DE GRAND VENT by Joseph Folliet.

Editions du Seuil, Paris, for "Bird Songs" ("Jacolino") from FLEURS DE MOUSSE by Francine Cockenpot.

Follett Publishing Co., Chicago, Illinois, for the poem "Spring Carnival" from SONGS FROM AROUND THE TOADSTOOL, by Rowena Bastin Bennett. Copyright 1930, 1937, by Follett Publishing Co., Chicago, Ill.

Hall and McCreary Co., for "January and February" from THE GOLDEN BOOK OF FAVORITE SONGS, copyright 1923 by Hall and McCreary Co. Used by permission.

Harcourt, Brace & Co., for "Hoosen Johnny" from THE AMERICAN SONGBAG by Carl Sandburg, and for "How To Tell Corn Fairies When You See Them" from ROOTABAGA STORIES by Carl Sandburg.

Harper and Brothers, for the poem "Old Log House" from A WORLD TO KNOW by James S. Tippett.

Harvard University Press, for "Dark Green Shawl" from ON THE TRAIL OF NEGRO FOLK SONG by Dorothy Scarborough.

Ralph Hess, for "My Corn Is Now Stretching Out Its Hands."

Henry Holt and Company, Inc., for "Somewhere" from COLLECTED POEMS OF WALTER DE LA MARE, copyright, 1920, by Henry Holt and Company; copyright, 1948, by Walter De La Mare. Used by permission of the publishers.

Ruth C. Koch, for the poem "The Cherry Tree" from LET US BE MERRY by Agnes Louise Dean, published by Alfred Knopf Inc.

John Lach, for "I'm a Tinker" from TREASURY OF SLOVAK FOLK SONGS, published by Crown Publishers.

Liveright Publishing Corp., for "Come, Dance with Me," from PLAYTIME WITH MUSIC by Abeson and Bailey, copyright 1952 by Liveright Publishing Corp.

Ruby Terrill Lomax, for "Ducks in the Millpond" from OUR SINGING COUNTRY and for "All the Pretty Little Horses" and "Hop Up, My Ladies" from AMERICAN BALLADS AND FOLK SONGS.

University of London Press, for "Invitation" ("Down by the Riverside") and "Draw a Pail of Water," both from INFANT JOY by Desmond MacMahon.

Longmans Green & Co. Ltd., for "Old Caspar" from SINGING CIRCLE by Lady Bell.

Oxford University Press, London, for "Carol of the Birds" translated by Percy Dearmer, from THE OXFORD BOOK OF CAROLS, and for "Spinning Wheel" from SIXTY SONGS FOR LITTLE CHILDREN. Both used by permission.

Theodore Presser & Co., for "Sheepshearing" from ONE HUNDRED ENGLISH FOLK SONGS, collected and arranged by Cecil J. Sharp. Copyright 1916 by Oliver Ditson Co. Used by permission.

G. P. Putnam's Sons, for the poems "Winter" and "Brooms" from EVERYTHING AND ANYTHING by Dorothy Aldis.

Rand, McNally & Co., for "Welcome" by Rose Waldo, published in Child Life.

G. Ricordi & Co., for "Little Train of Caipira" from BACHI-ANAS BRASILEIRAS NO. 2 by Heitor Villa-Lobos.

Estate of Norberto Romualdez, for the melody of "Canoe Song" ("Del Pasig las Aguas").

Schofield & Sims Ltd., for "Polly Parakeet" from A NEW WAY SONG BOOK by Desmond MacMahon.

G. Schirmer, Inc., for "The Shoemaker" from SPANISH SONGS OF OLD CALIFORNIA, collected and translated by Charles F. Lummis.

Arthur P. Schmidt, for thematic extracts of "Of a Tailor and a Bear" by Edward MacDowell.

Muriel Shideler, for her poem "Hayride."

Janet E. Tobitt, for "The Blacksmith" ("Twankydillo"), and "Down the Meadow" from THE DITTY BAG.

Findley Torrence, for the poem "Invitation" from COL-LECTED POEMS OF RIDGELY TORRENCE, published by The Macmillan Co.

United Synagogue Commission on Jewish Education, for "Hanu-kah Is Here!" by Freda Prensky, from SONGS OF CHILDHOOD.

John W. Work, for "Lady in the Pond."

The music in this book was reproduced from hand written originals by Maxwell Weaner

As I was going along, along,
A-singing a comical song, a song,
The road that I went was long, long, long
And so I went just a-singing along, along, along.
                              —UNKNOWN

Contents

SING AS YOU GO

Let's play we are a tune
And make a kind of song
About the sun and moon
Before the stars were born.
You be the breath, I'll be the horn,
It will not take us long.
        —RIDGELY TORRENCE

Hand in Hand

A Morning Hymn

OLD HYMN
GREGORIAN CHANT ARRANGED BY LOWELL MASON

1. Fa - ther, we thank Thee — for the — night;
2. Help us to do the — things we — should;

Thank Thee for pleas - ant — morn - ing — light;
Help us to be to — oth - ers — good;

Thank Thee for rest, for — food, for — care,
In all we do, in — work or — play,

For all that makes the day so — fair.
Lov - ing Thee bet - ter ev - 'ry — day.

1

Invitation

ENGLISH SINGING GAME

Find these musical figures in this song:

Play them on bells and sing them.

Down by the riv-er-side the green grass grows,

Where {Mar - y Ste - vens / Jim - my Wat - son} walks tip - toe.

{She / He} sings, {she / he} sings, {she / he} sings so sweet.

{She / He} calls, "Oh, come o - ver," a - cross the street.

"Su - sie, Da - vid, will you vis - it me?

Come next ___ {Mon - day / Tues - day} at half past three.

2

Tea cakes, pan - cakes, ev - 'ry - thing you see,

Won't we have a love - ly time at half past three?"

The More We Get Together

Clap hands on the strong beats.
Play the strong beats on triangle or tambourine.

WORDS ANONYMOUS
OLD GERMAN MELODY

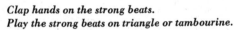

The more we get to - geth- er, to - geth- er, to - geth- er,

The more we get to - geth- er, the hap-pi- er we'll be.

For your friends are my friends, and my friends are your friends.

The more we get to - geth- er, the hap-pi- er we'll be.

Come Dance with Me

WORDS BY MARION ABESON
CREOLE FOLK TUNE

The melody bells begin this song and continue throughout the refrain:

Come dance with me, come dance with me,

While the mon-key plays the vi - o - lin.

Come dance with me, come dance with me,

While the mon-key plays the vi - o - lin.

1. Just sprin- kle pep - per on the fish -'s tail;

Makes it nice and sweet, might-y good to eat.

4

Just sprin - kle pep - per on the fish - 's tail;

Go back to the beginning

Makes it nice and sweet, might - y good to eat.

2. Now let it sizzle in the frying pan;
   Makes it good and brown, finest fish in town.
   Now let it sizzle in the frying pan;
   Makes it good and brown, finest fish in town.

3. Then chop some onion for a tasty sauce;
   Just a dash of spice makes it smell so nice.
   Then chop some onion for a tasty sauce;
   Just a dash of spice makes it smell so nice.

5

Oh, How Lovely Cooks the Meat

SOUTH AFRICAN FOLK SONG
COLLECTED BY JOSEF MARAIS

1. Oh, how love - ly cooks the meat,
2. Oh, how love - ly cooks the meat,

Oh, how love - ly cooks the meat, When I
Oh, how love - ly cooks the meat, In a

get back home to eat, How love - ly cooks the meat!
mo - ment I will eat, How love - ly cooks the meat!

I smell it far a - way, I
I'm com - ing through the door, I

think of it all day. She's cook-ing the meat for
can't wait an - y - more. At the ta - ble I take my

me, What a meal it's going to be!
seat, Put my teeth in - to that meat.

Clear the Kitchen

AS SUNG IN PENNSYLVANIA
BY EMMA KATURAH GRENOBLE

Sandblocks swish like brooms:

Down in Vir - gin - ia one aft - er - noon,

We swept the floor with a brand new broom;

And then we all would form a ring,

And this is the song that we would sing: __

"Clear the kitch-en, young folks, old folks, Clear the kitch-en,

young folks, old folks. Old Vir - gin - ia nev - er tires!"

Making Tortillas

ENGLISH WORDS BY LEO PARIS
BRAZILIAN FOLK SONG

To grind corn: *Use sandblocks or turn maracas from side to side*

To pat bread: *Clap hands first on right side and then on left*

1. When the corn is read - y, Juan Pi - ru - le - ro,
2. When the bat - ter's read - y, Juan Pi - ru - le - ro,

Juan Pi - ru - le - ro, What shall we do?

Find a stone and fol - low Juan Pi - ru - le - ro,
Toss it up and fol - low Juan Pi - ru - le - ro,

He'll grind and I'll grind and you will grind, too!
He'll pat and I'll pat and you will pat, too!

3. When the bread is patted, Juan Pirulero,
   Juan Pirulero, what shall we do?
   Light the fire and follow Juan Pirulero,
   He'll bake and I'll bake and you will bake, too.

4. When the bread is ready, Juan Pirulero,
   Juan Pirulero, what shall we do?
   Take it out and follow Juan Pirulero,
   He'll eat tortillas and you will eat, too.

From *Little Pedro and the Street Singers*, Record Album CRG 5028,
Children's Record Guild. Used by permission.

Clear the Line

FOLK SONG FROM ALABAMA

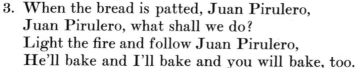

"Dial" 3 2 2 1 1 6 *on melody bells before you begin to sing*

You've got   to   clear   the   line be-fore you call,

You've got   to   clear   the   line be-fore you   call,

If   you   ev - er   want to   get   an   an - swer,

You've got   to   clear   the   line be-fore you   call.

9

Waddle-dee-dee

WORDS AND MUSIC BY JOSEPH D. CATALYNE

*Accompany this song with triangle,
drums, tone blocks and sand blocks.
Sing or play the "oompahs" before each stanza.*

Oom - pah, oom - pah, oom - pah, oom-pah-pah, oom-pah, oom - pah, oom - pah-pah.

1. Skat - ing and skat - ing to this old tune that's

plain to see, The wheels roll a - long and they

sing a song: Wad - dle - dee - dee.

Refrain

Skrim, skram, skrim, skree; jim, jam, wad- dle- dee- dee.

Skrim, skram, skrim, skree; jim, jam, wad - dle- dee- dee.

2. Bounce, catch and bounce, catch to this old tune that's plain to see,
   Oh, bounce, catch and bounce, catch; it's so much fun: Waddle-dee-dee.

10

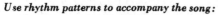

Use rhythm patterns to accompany the song:

Hi-dee-roon

CALYPSO SONG FROM JAMAICA

1. Come on ___ and show me, } Hi - dee-roon, ___ Oh!
2. Show me ___ your jump - ing,

Come on ___ and show me, } Hi - dee- roon, ___ Oh!
Show me ___ your jump - ing,

Come on ___ and show me, } Hi - dee- roon, ___ Oh!
Show me ___ your jump - ing,

Come on ___ and show me, } Hi - dee - roon. ___
Show me ___ your jump - ing,

3. Show me your skipping, Hi-dee-roon, Oh!

4. Show me your dancing, Hi-dee-roon, Oh!

5. Show me your clapping, Hi-dee-roon, Oh!

11

Polly Parakeet

SWISS FOLK SONG
ARRANGED BY DESMOND MacMAHON

1. In our house we have a pet,
2. Pol - ly wears up - on his head,

He's a gai - ly col - ored fel - low,
Hood of pur - ple trimmed with yel - low.

In our house we have a pet,
Pol - ly wears up - on his head,

He's a gai - ly col - ored fel - low.
Hood of pur - ple trimmed with yel - low.

Green as an - y grass are his long coat - tails,
Whit - er than the snow is his plum - age feather,

Red as an - y ru - by are his long toe - nails.
Black - er than the night __ is his tongue like leather.

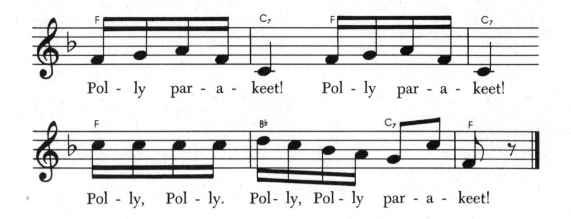

Pol - ly par - a - keet! Pol - ly par - a - keet!

Pol - ly, Pol - ly. Pol - ly, Pol - ly par - a - keet!

Bingo

AMERICAN FOLK SONG

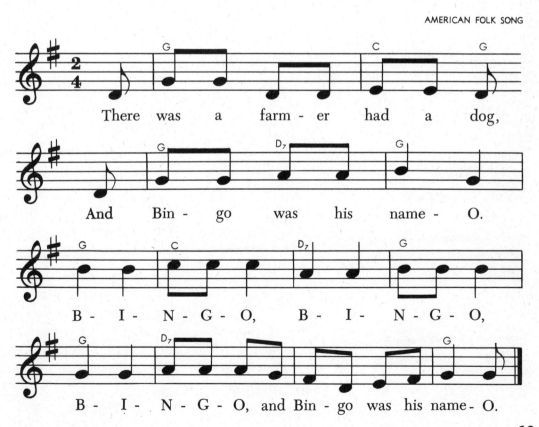

There was a farm - er had a dog,

And Bin - go was his name - O.

B - I - N - G - O, B - I - N - G - O,

B - I - N - G - O, and Bin - go was his name - O.

Swing High

WORDS BY PATIENCE STRONG
MUSIC BY HOAGY CARMICHAEL

*So will you come now and swing while I swing
And we'll sing all the songs that we love to sing.*
—ROSE WALDO

Play on piano or melody bells before and throughout

Swing   high,   swing   low,

Swing_high, swing_ low,

Down   to   the   ground   and   then

up   you   go,

Oh,   what   a   lot   of   the

world   you   see

O - ver   the   top   of   the

tree. _____ Swing high, swing low,

Just like a bird on the wing you go,

But what if the swing should swing you high,

(Small notes optional)

And leave you up there in the sky? _____

Cat in the Plum Tree

ENGLISH ROUND

Lady, come out and see, The

cat is in the plum tree.

Jack, Can I Ride?

ALABAMA FOLK SONG

Refrain

Jack, can I ride? Ho, ho, Jack,— can I ride? Ho, ho,

End here

Jack, can I ride? Ho, ho, Jack,— can I ride? Ho, ho.

Verse

1. Asked my ma-ma for fif-teen cents—
2. Asked my ma-ma for five cents more—

To see the el-e-phant jump the fence,
To see the el-e-phant climb the door,

Jumped so high till he hit the sky,—
He jumped so low he stumped his toe, —

Go back to the beginning

He could-n't get back till next Ju-ly.
And that was the end of the ele-phant show.

Mr. Rabbit

FOLK SONG FROM SOUTHERN UNITED STATES

1.
2. { "Mis - ter Rab - bit, Mis - ter Rab - bit,

Your ears might - y long!"
Your foot's might - y red!"

"Yes in - deed, they're put on wrong." —
"Yes in - deed, I'm al - most dead." —

Refrain

Ev - 'ry lit - tle soul must shine, shine, shine. —

Ev - 'ry lit - tle soul must shine, — shine, shine.

3. "Your coat's mighty gray!"
   "Yes indeed, 'twas made that way."

4. "Your tail's mighty white!"
   "Yes indeed, I'm going out of sight."

5. "You hop mighty high!"
   "Yes indeed, up to the sky."

In the Fashion

POEM BY A. A. MILNE
MUSIC BY HOAGY CARMICHAEL

A lion has a tail and a ver-y fine tail,

And so has an el-e-phant and so has a whale,

And so has a croc-o-dile, and so has a quail,

They've all got tails but me. If I had six-pence

I would buy one; I'd say to the shop-man,

"Let me try one"; I'd say to the el-e-phant,

18

"This is my one"; They'd all come round to see.

Then I'd say to the li - on,"Why, you've got a tail!

And so has the el - e-phant, and so has the whale!

And look! There's a croc-o- dile!__

He's got a tail!

You've all got tails like me!"

Jennie Jenkins

AMERICAN FOLK SONG

White, blue, red or pur-ple.

1. Will you wear white, oh my dear, oh my dear?

Oh, will you wear white,— Jen-nie Jen - kins?

I won't wear white for the col - or's too bright,

I'll— buy me a fol - de - rol - dy,

til - dy - tol - dy, seek - a - dou - ble

roll,———————— Jen - nie Jen - kins roll.———

20

2. Will you wear blue?
   I won't wear blue,
   The color's too true,

3. Will you wear red?
   I won't wear red,
   It's the color of my head,

4. Will you wear purple?
   I won't wear purple,
   It's the color of a turtle,

My White Mouse

ENGLISH WORDS BY LOUISE KESSLER
GERMAN FOLK SONG

Play "tip-tip-toes" on melody bells as you sing the refrain:

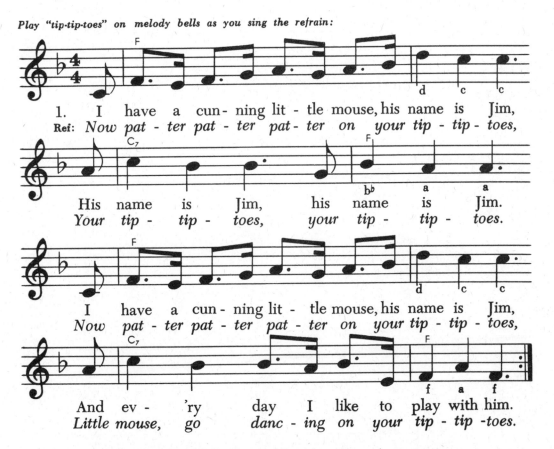

1. I have a cun - ning lit - tle mouse, his name is Jim,
Ref: *Now pat - ter pat - ter pat - ter on your tip - tip - toes,*

His name is Jim, his name is Jim.
Your tip - tip - toes, your tip - tip - toes.

I have a cun - ning lit - tle mouse, his name is Jim,
Now pat - ter pat - ter pat - ter on your tip - tip - toes,

And ev - 'ry day I like to play with him.
Little mouse, go danc - ing on your tip - tip - toes.

2. One night while I was sleeping, mousie ran away,
   I looked for him, I looked for him.
   One night while I was sleeping, mousie ran away.
   I looked inside a shoe and there was Jim!

21

Counting Out

FOLK SONG FROM THE BRITISH ISLES
COLLECTED BY JEAN RITCHIE

The wind, the wind, the wind blows high,

The snow comes fall - ing from the sky.

An - nie says she'd like to try,
John - ny says he'd like to try,

She's the girl of the gold - en cit - y.
He's the boy of the gold - en cit - y.

Begin to count out:

She is hand - some, she is pret - ty,
He is hand - some, he is wit - ty,

She is the girl of the gold - en cit - y,
He is the boy of the gold - en cit - y,

22

She shall choose,   one,   two,   three,
He shall choose,   one,   two,   three,

You are the one that it will be.

Borrowing

KENTUCKY FOLK SONG
COLLECTED BY JEAN THOMAS, THE "TRAIPSIN' WOMAN"

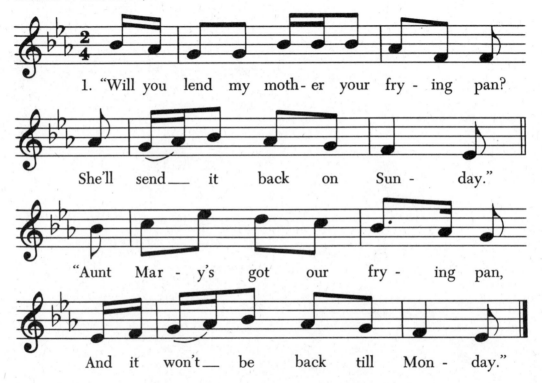

1. "Will you lend my moth-er your fry - ing pan?

She'll send___ it back on Sun - day."

"Aunt Mar - y's got our fry - ing pan,

And it won't___ be back till Mon - day."

2. "Can you lend my mother a pair of tongs?
   Our Johnny lost them playing."
   "My mother will not lend the tongs,
   That's what she's always saying."

3. "Will you lend my mother your washing stick?
   She wants to start her washing."
   "My mother won't lend you her washing stick,
   Our Mintie broke it, playing."

4. "Will you lend my mother your looking glass?
   My father broke ours, shaving."
   "Our Susan wants to do her hair,
   It's lovely, long and waving."

24

"Then you won't lend us your frying pan?"
"No!"
"Nor your tongs?"
"No!"
"Nor your washing stick?"
"No!"
"Nor your looking glass?"
"No!"
"Then will you lend us your cat to catch a lot of mice?"
"Yes, and she shall bring them to us!"

Three Dukes

AMERICAN SINGING GAME

A bugle call announces the horsemen:

(Use melody flutes, piano, or melody bells)

1. Here come three dukes a - rid - ing,} Rid - ing,
2. What are you rid - ing here for?}

rid - ing; {Here come three dukes a - rid - ing,}
{What are you rid - ing here for?}

Ran - som, pran - som, tan - tar - ry - O!

3. We're riding here to be married,
4. And which of us will you have, sirs?
5. You're all too slow and clumsy,
6. We're just as spry as you are,
7. You're all as stiff as pokers,
8. We can bend as well as you can,
9. The prettiest one is this one,

Turn the Glasses Over

AMERICAN SINGING GAME

I've been to Har - lem, I've been to Do - ver,

I've trav - eled this wide world all o - ver,

O - ver, o - ver, three times o - ver,

Drink what you have to drink and turn the glass - es o - ver.

26

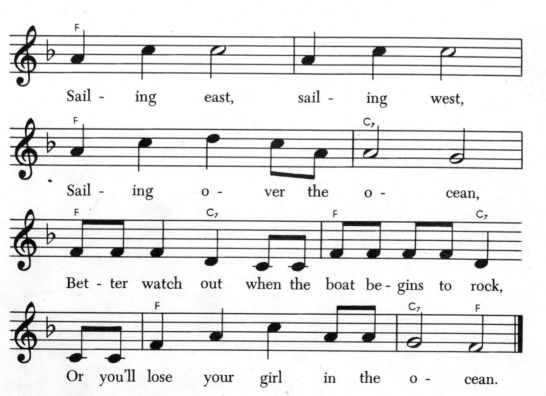

Sail - ing   east,   sail - ing   west,

Sail - ing   o - ver   the   o - cean,

Bet - ter watch   out   when the   boat be - gins   to   rock,

Or you'll lose   your   girl   in   the   o - cean.

Old Caspar

FROM "SINGING CIRCLE" BY LADY BELL

1. Old Cas - par had six sons so fine,

Old Cas - par he had daugh - ters nine;

Old Cas - par he was wont to say

To sons and daugh - ters, ev - 'ry day,

"Watch me, watch me, morn- ing noon and night!

Do ev - 'ry-thing that I do, then you will be right."

2. Old Caspar he would walk about,
   And first look in and then look out;
   Old Caspar he would say "Good day!"
   Put on his coat and then would say,

3. Old Caspar would put on his hat,
   And first do this and then do that;
   And go this way and go that way,
   And so, and so, and then would say,

Let Us Be Dancing

FLEMISH FOLK SONG

Play encircled notes on melody bells while you sing:

Ro - sa, let us be danc - ing, be danc - ing, be danc - ing,

Ro - sa, let us be danc - ing, be danc - ing   now.

Round the cir - cle Ro - sa goes, Danc - ing light - ly

on   her toes, Then turns   a - round.____

Three Pirates

ENGLISH FOLK SONG

1. Three pi - rates came to Lon - don town, Yo ho, yo ho.
2. At first they came to a way - side inn, Yo ho, yo ho.

Three pi - rates came to Lon - don town, Yo ho, yo ho.
At first they came to a way - side inn, Yo ho, yo ho.

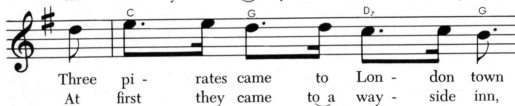

Three pi - rates came to Lon - don town
At first they came to a way - side inn,

To see the King put on his crown.
And said, "Good land - lord, let us in."

Yo ho, you lub - bers, Yo ho,

you lub - bers, Yo ho, yo ho, yo ho!

30

3. "O landlord, have you hoards of gold,
   Yo ho, yo ho.
   O landlord, have you hoards of gold,
   Yo ho, yo ho.
   O landlord, have you hoards of gold,
   Enough to fill the afterhold?"

4. "O yes sir, I have hoards of gold,
   Enough to fill the afterhold."

5. "O landlord, have you a daughter fair,
   With laughing eyes and curly hair?"

6. "O yes sir, I've a daughter fair,
   With laughing eyes and curly hair."

7. "O landlord, will she marry me,
   And sail with me across the sea?"

8. "O yes sir, she will marry thee,
   And sail with thee across the sea."

Jackfish

FOLK SONG FROM THE SOUTHERN APPALACHIANS

1. That old jack-fish swim-ming up the stream,
2. Fish-pole broke and I ___ got ___ mad,

I asked that jack-fish what did he mean.
And down to the bot-tom went old ___ dad.

Just bait-ed a hook to catch a shad,
I grabbed ___ that jack-fish by the snout,

The ___ first thing he bit was my old dad.
And ___ turned that ___ jack-fish wrong side out.

Sing fal de rol de ee - do, ee - do eye - do,

Fal de rol de ee - do, ee - do - eye. ee - do - eye.

Play these notes on bells or piano throughout the song:

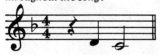

Louisiana Lullaby

FOLK SONG FROM LOUISIANA

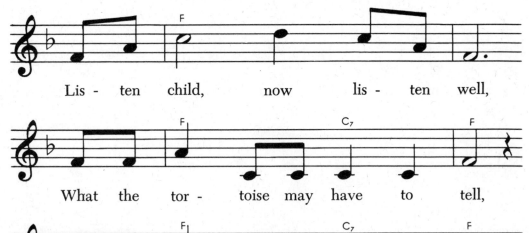

1. Dream-land o-pens here, Sweep the dream path clear.

Lis - ten child, now lis - ten well,

What the tor - toise may have to tell,

What the tor - toise may have to tell.

2. Dreamland opens here,
   Sweep the dream path clear.
   Listen child, dear little child,
   To the song of the crocodile,
   To the song of the crocodile.

3. Dreamland opens here,
   Sweep the dream path clear.
   Listen child, now close your eyes,
   In the cane-break the wild cat cries,
   In the cane-break the wild cat cries.

The Frog and the Mouse

AMERICAN FOLK SONG

1. There was a frog lived in a well,

Whip - see did - dle dee dan - dy O!

There was a mouse lived in a mill,

Whip - see did - dle dee dan - dy O!

This frog he would a - woo - ing ride, With

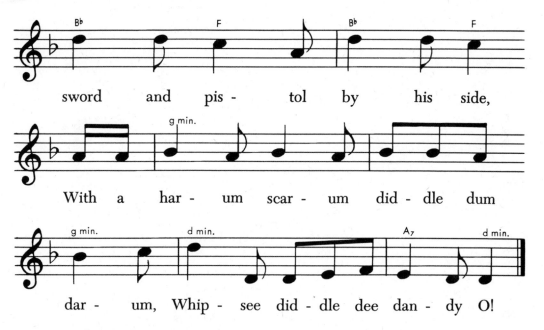

sword and pis - tol by his side,

With a har - um scar - um did - dle dum

dar - um, Whip - see did - dle dee dan - dy O!

2. He rode till he came to Mouse's Hall,
   Whipsee diddle dee dandy O!
   Where he most tenderly did call,
   Whipsee diddle dee dandy O!
   "O, Mistress Mouse, are you at home?
   And if you are, oh, please come down."
   With a harum scarum diddle dum darum,
   Whipsee diddle dee dandy O!

3. "My Uncle Rat is not at home,
   I dare not for my life come down."
   Then Uncle Rat he soon comes home,
   "And who's been here since I've been gone?"

4. "Here's been a fine young gentleman,
   Who swears he'll have me if he can."
   Then Uncle Rat gave his consent
   And made a handsome settlement.

5. Four partridge pies with season made,
   Two potted larks and marmalade,
   Four woodcocks and a venison pie.
   I would that at that feast were I.

Ten Little Danish Boys

WORDS BY EARL ROGERS
DANISH FOLK SONG

1. Ten lit - tle Dan- ish boys Rid- ing on a bike;
2. Nine lit - tle Dan- ish boys Play- ing near the gate;

One had to go right home, And then there were nine.
One had to milk the cow, And then there were eight.

There was one lit - tle, two lit - tle, three lit - tle,

3. Eight little Danish boys,
   Looking at the heavens;
   One got a cinder in his eye,
   Leaving seven.

4. Seven little Danish boys,
   Practicing some tricks;
   One had to rest awhile,
   And then there were six.

5. Six little Danish boys,
   Learning how to dive;
   One didn't like the water,
   Then there were five.

6. Five little Danish boys,
   Playing in a store;
   One ate too many cookies,
   Then there were four.

four lit - tle, five lit - tle Dan - ish boys;

There were six lit - tle, seven lit - tle, eight lit - tle,

nine lit - tle, ten lit - tle Dan - ish boys.

7. Four little Danish boys,
   Hollering with glee;
   One got a little hoarse,
   And then there were three.

8. Three little Danish boys,
   Wond'ring what to do;
   One stopped to fly a kite,
   And then there were two.

9. Two little Danish boys,
   Playing in the sun;
   One went to catch some fish,
   And then there was one.

10. One little Danish boy
    Tried to have some fun;
    Scared folks on Hallowe'en,
    And then there were none.

FENCES AND CURBSTONES

Out in the Country

The Cherry Tree

POEM BY AGNES LOUISE DEAN
MUSIC BY ARTHUR C. EDWARDS

Play last phrase on melody bells to begin and end this song:

Player 1 asks a question   Player 2 answers

1. White in the sun - shine, white in the rain;
2. Red in the sun - shine, red in the rain;

Lean - ing out from the wall at the
Lean - ing out from the wall at the

top of the lane, The cher - ry tree
top of the lane, The cher - ry tree

watch - es the peo - ple who go
watch - es the peo - ple who go

Down the hill fast; up the hill slow.
Down the hill fast; up the hill slow.

39

Wind in the Corn

POEM BY MARGARET WISE BROWN
MUSIC BY MILTON KAYE

"Slide" up and down the melody bells or autoharp
to imitate the sound of gentle wind:

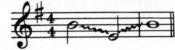

I heard the wind _____ in the corn one day,

I knew that it came _____ from far a - way.

And it rus - tled the trem - bling corn to say

That it was go - ing far a - way

And could not stay, _____

Could nev - er stay. _____

40

If you look close and if you listen close you can see the corn fairies come dancing and singing—sometimes. If it is a wild day and a hot sun is pouring down while a cool north wind blows—and this happens sometimes—then you will be sure to see thousands of corn fairies marching and countermarching in mocking grand marches over the big, long blanket of green and silver. Then too they sing, only you must listen with your littlest and newest ears if you wish to hear their singing. They sing soft songs that go pla-sizzy pla-sizzy-sizzy, and each song is softer than an eye-wink, softer than a Nebraska baby's thumb.

—From "How To Tell Corn Fairies
When You See Them" by Carl Sandburg

Farmer's Prayer

WORDS AND MUSIC BY DONALD SHERRARD

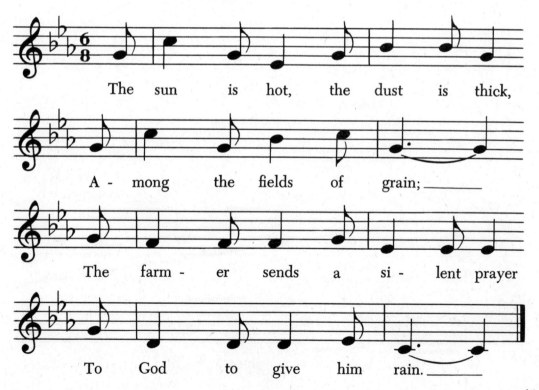

The sun is hot, the dust is thick,

A - mong the fields of grain;

The farm - er sends a si - lent prayer

To God to give him rain.

My Farm

ARGENTINIAN FOLK SONG

1. 2. I have a lit - tle farm be - side a wind - ing stream,

I have a lit - tle barn-yard where the grass is green.

There the {chick - ens / duck - lings} go like this: {Cluck, cluck, / Quack, quack,}

There the {chick - ens / duck - lings} go like this: {Cluck, cluck. / Quack, quack.}

They come on the run, they come on the run,

When the farm - er gives them {corn, / wheat,}

They come on the run, they come on the run,

When the farm - er gives them { corn. } { wheat. }

3. There the horses go like this:
   Neigh, neigh.
   They come on the run,
   When the farmer gives them oats.

4. There the donkeys go like this:
   Hee-haw.
   They come on the run,
   When the farmer gives them hay.

5. There the piglets go like this:
   Oink - oink.
   They come on the run,
   When the farmer gives them whey.

6. There the puppies go like this:
   Woof, woof.
   They come on the run,
   When the farmer gives them bones.

7. There the kittens go like this:
   Meow, meow.
   They come on the run,
   When the farmer gives them milk.

8. There the milk-cows go like this:
   Moo, moo.
   They come on the run,
   When the farmer gives them hay.

43

Sheepshearing

ENGLISH FOLK SONG

Play on bells before you start to sing:

1. How de-light-ful to see, In the eve-nings in spring,

The __ sheep go-ing home to the fold. ____

The __ mas-ter doth sing, As he views ev-'ry-thing,

And his dog goes be-fore him where told, ____

And his dog goes be-fore him where told. ____

2. The sixth month of the year,
In the month called June,
When the weather's too hot to be borne,
The master doth say,
As he goes on his way:
"Tomorrow my sheep shall be shorn,
Tomorrow my sheep shall be shorn."

3. Now as for those sheep,
   They're delightful to see,
   They're a blessing to a man on his farm;
   For their flesh it is good,
   It's the best of all food,
   And the wool it will clothe us up warm.

4. Now, the sheep they're all shorn,
   And the wool carried home,
   Here's a health to our master and flock;
   And if we should stay,
   Till the last goes away,
   I'm afraid 'twill be past twelve o'clock.

Ducks in the Millpond

FOLK SONG FROM VIRGINIA

1. Ducks in the mill-pond and geese in the clo - ver, I
2. Ducks in the mill-pond and geese in the clo - ver, They

jumped in - to bed and the bed turned right o - ver,
swam in the pond and they got wet all o - ver,

Hi - ho! Gon - na get on a rink - tum,

Hi - ho! Gon - na get on a rink - tum.

Hoosen Johnny

FOLK SONG FROM ILLINOIS

1. The lit-tle black bull came down the mead-ow,
2. First— he pawed and then he bel-lowed,

Hoo - sen John - ny, Hoo - sen John - ny,

46

The lit - tle black bull came down the mead-ow,
𝄼 First __ he pawed and then he bel- lowed,

Long time a - go.

Long time a - go, long time a - go,

The lit - tle black bull came down the mead-ow,
𝄼 First __ he pawed and then he bel - lowed,

Long time a - go.

3. He whet his horn on a white
    oak sapling,
   Hoosen Johnny, Hoosen Johnny,
   He whet his horn on a white
    oak sapling,
   Long time ago.

4. He shook his tail, he jarred
    the river,
   Hoosen Johnny, Hoosen Johnny,
   He shook his tail, he jarred
    the river,
   Long time ago.

5. He pawed the dirt in the heifers' faces,
   Hoosen Johnny, Hoosen Johnny,
   He pawed the dirt in the heifers' faces,
   Long time ago.

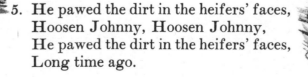

Tinga Layo

CALYPSO SONG FROM THE WEST INDIES

Tin - ga Lay - o! Come, lit - tle don - key, come;

Tin - ga Lay - o! Come, lit - tle don - key, come.

1. My don - key walk, my don - key talk, my
2. My don - key eat, my don - key sleep, my

don - key eat with a knife and fork.
don - key kick with his two hind feet.

Tin - ga Lay - o! Come, lit - tle don - key, come

Tin - ga Lay - o! Come, lit - tle don - key,

48

Sandy Land

PLAY-PARTY SONG FROM OKLAHOMA

1. Make my liv - in' in sand - y land,

Make my liv - in' in sand - y land,

Make my liv - in' in sand - y land,

La - dies, fare you well.

2. One big tractor to plow the land,
   Ladies, fare you well.

3. Raise sweet potatoes in sandy land,
   Ladies, fare you well.

4. Dig sweet potatoes in sandy land,
   Ladies, fare you well.

5. Trucking sweet potatoes into town,
   Ladies, fare you well.

Calling the Cows

SWISS FOLK SONG

Play these tones on the piano as you sing

Go call the brown one, go call the black one,

They must all come, they must all come;

Go call the Swiss cow, go call the Jer - sey,

They must all come in - to the barn.

Hol - dee-ree-dee- ah, dee- ah, hol-dee-ree-dee- ah, ho,

Hol - dee -ree-dee- ah, dee- ah, hol- dee-ree-dee- ah, ho,

Hol - dee-ree-dee- ah, dee - ah, hol-dee-ree-dee-ah, ho,

Hol - dee- ree - dee - ah, dee - ah, ho!

There Was a Man and He Was Mad

FOLK SONG FROM OHIO

1. There was a man and he was mad,
And he jumped in - to the pud - ding bag.

2. The pud - ding bag it was so thick
That he jumped in - to a walk - ing stick.

3. The walking stick it was so narrow
That he jumped into an old wheel barrow.

4. The wheel barrow it did so crack
That he jumped onto a horse's back.

5. The horse's back it did so bend
That he jumped into a taching*end.

6. The taching end it was so rotten
That he jumped into a bag of cotton.

7. The bag of cotton it set on fire
And blew him up to Jeremiah.

Spoken: Pouf! Pouf! Pouf!

*An "attaching end," as of harness.

Supper on the Ground

SOUTHERN PICNIC SONG

1. All the day a - sing - ing, ____ (All the day a - sing - ing)

Sup - per on the ground, _____ (Sup - per on the ground)

Old - er folks and young - uns ____ (Old - er folks and young-uns)

Gath - ered a - round. *(Gath-ered a - round)* Ev - 'ry kind of

vit - tle *(Ev - 'ry kind of vit - tle)* You ev - er did

see.___ *(Ev - er did see ___)* Come a - long, Mar - y, ___

___ *(Come a - long Mar - y)* and set ___ by me. *(And set _ by me.)*

2. Come along from Gloucester,
And from Toxaway,
Come on in the morning,
Stay here all day.
Bring along your fiddle,
Your dad's guitar too.
Come along, Mary, and set by me.

3. Bring some watermelon,
And some choc'late cake,
Bring some rolls and chicken,
All you can make.
All your friends and neighbors
You surely will see.
Come along, Mary, and set by me.

From SMOKY MOUNTAIN BALLADS, collected by Adelaide Van Wey and Donald Moore. Copyright 1946, assigned 1949 t Omega Music Edition, New York. International copyright secured. Reprinted by permission.

Roving Cowboy

AMERICAN COWBOY SONG

Coconut shell: = one shell turned from side to side on table top

F

1. Oh, I'm a rov-ing cow-boy
2. Come all you rov-ing cow-boys,

F   C₇   F

From off the west-ern plains,
Come with me while I roam.

F

My trade is cinch-ing sad-dles
I'm leav-ing dad and moth-er,

F   C₇   F

And pull-ing bri-dle reins.
Two sis-ters, and a home.

Play coconut shells on table top for sound of bronco's hoofs

I can throw a las - so
I'll ride through the moun - tains,

With skill and grace - ful ease,
Through des - ert and through cold;

And I can rope a bron - co,
I'll fol - low long-horned cat - tle,

And ride him where I please.
A life that's free and bold.

My Home's in Montana

WORDS ADAPTED BY W. S. WILLIAMS
AMERICAN COWBOY SONG

1. My home's in Mon-tan - a, I left In - di - an - a

To start a new life Far a - way in the West;

My skin's rough as leath - er, Made tough by the weath-er;

The wind and the sun Of the land I love best.

2. I learned how to lasso
   Way down in El Paso,
   I've followed the cattle
   Wherever they roam;
   I'm weary of straying,
   Right here I'll be staying,
   I'll wander no more
   For Montana's my home.

Farmers' Market

WORDS AND MUSIC BY NATIVIDAD VACIO

1. Farm - er's truck   un - loads there, where, oh,   where?

At   the Farm - ers' Mar - ket where they sell _____

Ap - ples, pears, choc - 'late bears, pump - kins,   too.

Come a - long with me,   then,   to   the Farm - ers' Mar - ket.

2. Fairfax bus takes you there, where, oh, where?
   To the Farmers' Market where they sell
   Fruits and meats, pickled beets, pizza, too.
   Come along with me, then, to the Farmers' Market.

3. Park your car over there, where, oh, where?
   At the Farmers' Market where they sell
   Coonskin caps, ranger hats, cowboy boots.
   Come along with me, then, to the Farmers' Market.

Along the Busy Street

Olvera Street Serenade

GROUP OF CHILDREN, VALLEY VIEW SCHOOL,
LOS ANGELES, CALIFORNIA

1. We had a gay time ___ On Ol - ve - ra Street, ___
2. We heard the gay songs ___ of Mex - i - co, ___

Where *se - ño - ri - tas* ___ and *se - ñors* meet, ___
Songs of *ma - ña - nas* ___ of long a - go. ___

Where chil - dren dance ___ and sing all day, ___
While vi - o - lins played sweet mel - o - dies ___

And 'round the gay ___ *pu - es - tos* play.
And ser - e - nades rich in har - mo - nies.

Señoritas (sayn-yo-ree-tas) young ladies
Señors (sayn-yors) young men
Puestos (poo-ays-tos) vendors' booths
Mañanas (mah-nya-nahs) mornings

Castanets, maracas, and tambourines begin song and play throughout

58

My Twenty Pennies

TRANSLATION BY J. OLCUTT SANDERS
VENEZUELAN FOLK SONG

1. With twen-ty pen-nies, with twen-ty pen-nies, with twen-ty
1. *Con real y me-dio, con real y me-dio, con real y*

pen-nies I bought a *pa-va.* The *pa-va* had a *pa-*
me-dio com-pré un-a pa-va. La pa-va tu-vo un pa-

vi-to, I have the *pa-va* and the *pa-vi-to;*
vi-to Ten-go la pa-va, ten-go el pa-vi-to;

And thus I have yet my twen-ty pen-nies.
Y siem-pre me que-da mi real y me-dio.

Each new verse introduces a different animal. (See below.) After the first verse, when we come to the * we use the repeat marks to include all previously mentioned animals, in reverse order.

1. *Pava* (turkey), *pavito* (baby turkey)
2. *Gata* (cat), *gatito* (kitten)
3. *Chiva* (goat), *chivito* (little goat)
4. *Mona* (monkey), *monito*.
5. *Lora* (parrot), *lorito*.
6. *Vaca* (cow), *vaquito*.

Where Bread Comes From

WORDS BY LISBETH E. RAWSKI
MUSIC BY MILTON KAYE

1. I go to the store each day to buy a loaf of bread.

It's piled on the shelf,

I reach and help my-self,

I reach and help my-self.

Refrain

Oh, I nev-er knew how man-y things there were to do,

Be - fore the wheat that the farm - er grows

Be - comes a loaf of bread for me and you.

2. Farmers are busy men,
   They have so much to do,
   To grow tons of wheat
   For all the bread we eat,
   For all the bread we eat.

3. Springtime is ploughing time,
   The farmer sows his seed.
   He carefully sows
   In straight and even rows,
   In straight and even rows.

4. Summer is harvest time,
   The farmer cuts the wheat.
   He threshes the grain
   And loads it on a train,
   And loads it on a train.

5. Then off to the mill it goes,
   It's trucked there from the train.
   The grinding machine
   Makes flour, white and clean,
   Makes flour, white and clean.

6. Now to the baker who
   Will make it into dough.
   With yeast and with salt,
   With water, milk and malt,
   With water, milk and malt.

7. Each fresh loaf of bread
   Is wrapped in paper right away,
   Of red, white, or green,
   To keep it nice and clean,
   To keep it nice and clean.

8. (Repeat verse 1.)

The Shoemaker

TRANSLATION BY CHARLES F. LUMMIS
FOLK SONG FROM SPANISH CALIFORNIA

I ___ spoke to a shoe-mak-er, For to

make me a pair of shoes-es, With the toes all nice-ly

round-ed Like a duck's bill or a goos-e's.

Con-found that old shoe-mak-er,

How he fooled me, though! He made me up the

shoes-es, But not the duck-bill toe!

Play these notes on bells:

He goes ris,   We go ras,

The Carpenter

ENGLISH WORDS BY LEO PARIS
BRAZILIAN FOLK SONG

1. The car - pen - ter is work - ing, saw - ing his lum - ber;

I   like to watch him work - ing, Saw - ing his lum - ber.

He goes ris,   We go ras,   He goes ris,   We go ras,

Un - til he's cut his lum - ber, Then   ev -'ry -one stop.

2. The scissor grinder's working,
   Grinding the scissors;
   I like to watch him working,
   Grinding his scissors.
   He goes bz-z-z,
   We go whiz-z-z,
   He goes bz-z-z,
   We go whiz-z-z,
   Until he's ground the scissors,
   Then everyone stop.

3. The mason is working,
   Mixing his mortar;
   I like to watch him working,
   Mixing his mortar.
   He goes push,
   We go woosh,
   He goes push,
   We go woosh,
   Until he's made his plaster,
   Then everyone stop.

From *Little Pedro and the Street Singers*, Record Album CRG 5028, Children's Record Guild. Used by permission.

Merry-Go-Round

WORDS BY MAY MORGAN
MUSIC BY HOAGY CARMICHAEL

Um bloop, bloop, um bloop, bloop, um bloop, bloop, bloop.

Hear the mu - sic make a bloop - y, bloop - y,

jin - gle, jan - gle sound;___ See the hor - ses go a -

pranc - ing and a - danc - ing all a - round!___

We will pay the man our mon - ey,

then we'll ride and ride and ride,

On the ver - y mer - ry mer - ry - go - round,

Rid - ing side by side, bloop, bloop!

Circus Parade

WORDS AND MUSIC BY MILTON KAYE

Play, as marked, on drum with soft beater

1. Oh, here comes the cir - cus band,
2. Oh, here come the el - e - phants,

Ta - ra - ra - ra, ta - ra - ra - ra - ra,
Clump - clump - ta - ra clump - clump - ta - ra - ra,

Here comes the cir - cus band,
Here come the el - e - phants,

Ta - ra - ra - ra - ra - ra!
Clump - clump - ta - ra - ra - ra!

Zing! Zing! _____ Zing! Zing! _____

Ta - ra - ra - ra, Ta - ra - ra - ra

Oh, how much I love the cir - cus, Ta - ra - ra! Boom! Boom!

Street Musicians

FRENCH FOLK SONG

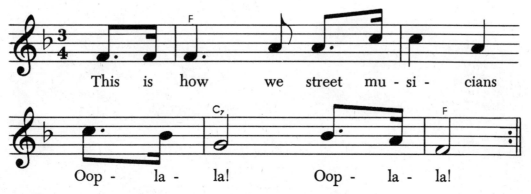

This is how we street mu-si-cians

Oop - la - la! Oop - la - la!

Spoken:

1. Play the trumpet! *Jouons de la trompette!*
(Zhoo-on de la trom-pette)

Ta - ta - ta, ta - ta - ta, ta - ta - ta,

Ta - ta - ta, ta - ta - ta. Ta - ta - ta,

ta - ta - ta, ta - ta - ta, Ta - ta - ta.

2. Play the violin! (*du violon*—vee-o-lon) Fee-lee-lee

3. Play the trombone! (*du trombone*—trom-bone) Toom-toom-pah

"OFF TO SOMEWHERE"

On Foot

Marching Along

SPIRITUAL

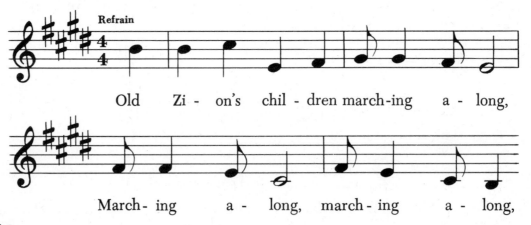

Old   Zi - on's   chil - dren march-ing   a - long,

March- ing   a - long,   march - ing   a - long,

I want to be off to Somewhere
To far, lone, lovely Somewhere,
No matter where Somewhere is.
                    —WALTER DE LA MARE

Old Zi - on's chil - dren march-ing a - long,

Talk - ing a - bout the wel - come day.

Verse

1. I hailed my moth- er in the morn - ing,
2. Oh, don't you want to live up yon - der,

March - ing a - long, march - ing a - long.

I hailed my moth- er in the morn - ing,
Oh, don't you want to live up yon - der,

Talk - ing a - bout the wel - come day.

69

Sing Along

TRADITIONAL

Make up your own accompaniment with rhythm instruments.

Sing a - long, oh, sing a - long, At work or while at play.

Though skies be gray and dull the day, Just

sing a - long the way! Sing a - long, oh, sing a - long, 'Twill

make the sad heart gay. You'll al - ways find the sun - shine

If you'll sing a - long the way.

Walking down the Roadway

ENGLISH WORDS BY ELEANOR GRAHAM VANCE
MUSIC BY S. MINGEOLET

*Play this introduction
on melody instruments:*

1. Walk-ing down the road - way, Un - der skies of gray,

Walk-ing down the road - way, Sing- ing all the way,

"I go the way the road goes."

2. Though the rain is falling,
   Though the way is long,
   Though the rain is falling,
   Still I sing my song,
   "I go the way the road goes."

3. In the golden sunset
   At my journey's end,
   In the golden sunset
   I shall find my friend.
   I go the way the road goes.

71

In Cars

John Brown Had a Little Indian

AMERICAN FOLK SONG

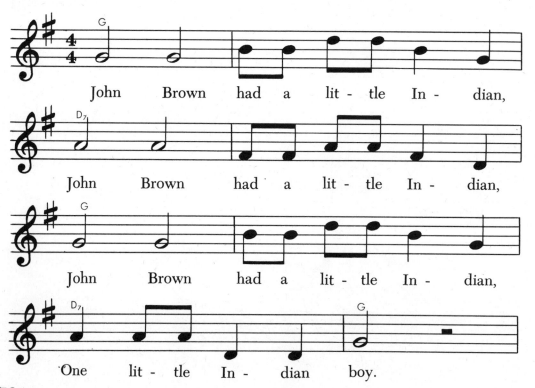

John Brown had a lit - tle In - dian,

John Brown had a lit - tle In - dian,

John Brown had a lit - tle In - dian,

One lit - tle In - dian boy.

One lit - tle, two lit - tle, three lit - tle In - dians,

Four lit - tle, five lit - tle, six lit - tle In - dians,

Sev'n lit - tle, eight lit - tle, nine lit - tle In - dians,

Ten lit - tle In - dian boys.

Ten Miles from Home

KENTUCKY FOLK SONG
COLLECTED BY JEAN THOMAS

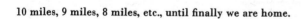
10 miles, 9 miles, 8 miles, etc., until finally we are home.

1. We're ten miles from home, We're ten miles from home.

We'll walk a while, we'll ride a while, We're ten miles from home.

73

Jig Along Home

WORDS AND MUSIC BY WOODY GUTHRIE

Jig, jig-a-jig, jig-a-jig a-long home, Jig, jig-a-jig, jig-a jig a-long home, Jig a-long, jig a-long, jig a-long home, Jig, jig-a-jig, jig-a-jig a-long home.

1. I went to the dance and the an-i-mals came,

The jay-bird danced with his horse-shoes on,

The grass-hop-per danced till he fell on the floor,

Jig a-long, jig-a-long, jig-a-long home.

2. The fish did a dance to the Fishing Reel,
   The lobster danced on the peacock's tail,
   The baboon danced with the rising moon,
   Jig along, jig along, jig along home.

3. The boards did rattle and the house did shake,
   The clouds did laugh and the world did quake,
   The new moon rattled some silver spoons,
   Jig along, jig along, jig along home.

4. The nails blew loose, the floor broke down,
   Everybody danced around and around,
   The house fell down, the crowd went home,
   Jig along, jig along, jig along home.

Are You Sleeping?

TRADITIONAL

Wake Brother John with the bells:

Are you sleep - ing, Are you sleep - ing?
Frè - re Jac - ques, Frè - re Jac - ques,

Broth - er John, Broth - er John?
Dor - mez vous, Dor - mez vous?

Morn-ing bells are ring - ing, Morn-ing bells are sing - ing,

Ding ding dong, Ding ding dong.

Get on Board

SPIRITUAL

Here comes the train:

Chooka chooka chooka chooka Toot toot toot toot

Refrain

Get on board, lit-tle chil-dren,

Get on board, lit-tle chil-dren,

Get on board, lit-tle chil-dren,

End here

There's room for man-y-a more.

76

1. The gos-pel train's a-com-ing, I hear it just at hand,___
2. I hear the train a-com-ing, She's com-ing round the curve,___

Go back to the beginning

I hear the car-wheels rum-bling And roll-ing through the land. So
She's loosen'd all her steam and brakes, And strain-ing ev-'ry nerve, Oh,

Little Train of Caipira

When the little train goes at full speed, you can hear
this rhythm played by maracas, scrapers and cellos.

FROM BACHIANAS BRASILEIRAS, NO. 2
HEITOR VILLA-LOBOS

The Dummy Line

FOLK SONG FROM SOUTHERN UNITED STATES

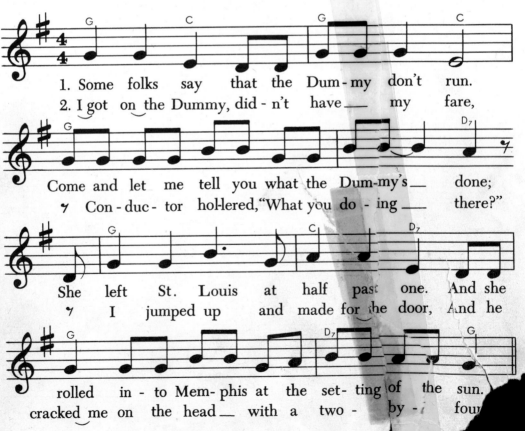

1. Some folks say that the Dum-my don't run.
2. I got on the Dummy, did-n't have __ my fare,

Come and let me tell you what the Dum-my's __ done;
Con-duc-tor hol-lered, "What you do - ing __ there?"

She left St. Louis at half past one. And she
I jumped up and made for the door, And he

rolled in - to Mem-phis at the set-ting of the sun.
cracked me on the head __ with a two - by - four

On the Dum-my,_____ on the Dum-my line,

Rise and shine. Rise and shine and pay your fine,

When you're rid-ing on the Dum-my,

on the Dum-my, Dum-my line.

3. I hopped off the Dummy and I lit on the track,
   Dragged my feet and scraped my back.
   I came to life and slung my dogs,
   Looked for sure like I'm on the hog.*

4. Some folks say that the Dummy don't run;
   Come and let me tell you what the Dummy's done.
   She left St. Louis at half-past two,
   But I walked to Memphis 'fore the Dummy came through.

*Down on one's luck.

Fly in the Sky

WORDS AND MUSIC BY MILTON KAYE

Play on piano (an octave lower) to
warm engine and keep plane in flight.

1. Buzz - ing like a fly, ___

Dron - ing there so high, ___ Hum - ming in the sky, ___

Ti - ny far - off plane, ti - ny plane.

To end song — as the plane climbs — play as high as you can on the piano, ending on high F.

2. Roaring in my ear,
   Screaming loud and clear,
   Zooming very near,
   What a giant plane, giant plane!

3. Growling in its flight,
   Soaring like a kite,
   Speeding out of sight,
   Good-bye, little plane, little plane.

80

By Boat

The Foghorn

WORDS AND MUSIC BY EVELYN H. HUNT

Play the first line and the last line on bells or piano.
Imitate the foghorn in the harbor or at the airport.

1. Fog is in the air - port,
2. Fog is in the har - bor,
Whoo, whoo, whoo.

The planes are circ - ling slow - ly,
The boats are mov - ing slow - ly,
Whoo, whoo, whoo.

The fog - horn blows, it sounds so far a - way,

The fog is thick, no sun will shine to - day.

Fog is in the air - port,
Fog is in the har - bor,
Whoo, whoo, whoo.

Lukey's Boat

CANADIAN FOLK SONG

1. Oh, Lu - key's boat is paint - ed green,
2. Oh, Lu - key's boat got a fine fore cutty,

A - ha, me b'ys!
A - ha, me b'ys!

Oh, Lu - key's boat is paint - ed green,
Oh, Lu - key's boat got a fine fore cutty,

From FOLK SONGS OF CANADA. Used by permission of Waterloo Music Company, Ontario.

The fin - est boat you've ev - er seen,
And ev - 'ry seam is chinked with putty,

A - ha, me rid - dle - I - day!
A - ha, me rid - dle - I - day!

3. Oh, Lukey's boat got a high stopped jib,
   A-ha, me b'ys!
   Oh, Lukey's boat got a high stopped jib
   And a patent block to her foremast head,
   A-ha, me riddle-I-day!

4. Oh, Lukey's boat got cotton sails,
   A-ha, me b'ys!
   Oh, Lukey's boat got cotton sails,
   And planks put on with galvanized nails,
   A-ha, me riddle-I-day!

5. Oh, Lukey's rolling out his grub,
   A-ha, me b'ys!
   Oh, Lukey's rolling out his grub,
   A barrel, a bag, and a ten-pound tub,
   A-ha, me riddle-I-day!

6. Oh, Lukey he sailed down the shore,
   A-ha, me b'ys!
   Oh, Lukey he sailed down the shore
   To catch some fish from Labrador,
   A-ha, me riddle-I-day!

"Me b'ys" is my boys.
When Lukey's boat is far out at sea, the little boat riding behind
it in the picture (a "cutty") is carried on the forward deck. The
sail flying before the mast (a "jib") is "high stopped"—that is,
almost as tall as the mast itself.

Blow, Boys, Blow

NEW ENGLAND SEA CHANTEY

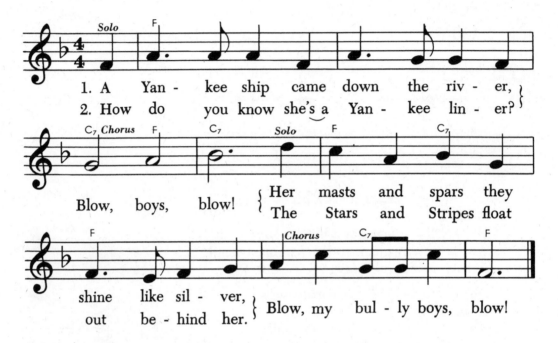

1. A Yan - kee ship came down the riv - er,
2. How do you know she's a Yan - kee lin - er?

Blow, boys, blow!
Her masts and spars they
The Stars and Stripes float

shine like sil - ver,
out be - hind her.
Blow, my bul - ly boys, blow!

3. And who d'you think is the captain of her?
   Why, Bully Hayes is the captain of her.

4. And what d'you think they've got for dinner?
   Pickled eels' feet and bullock's liver.

5. Blow, boys, blow, the sun's drawing water;
   Three cheers for the cook and one for his daughter.

6. Then blow, my bullies, all together,
   Blow, my boys, for better weather.

Canoe Song

WORDS BY MARGARET MARKS
PHILIPPINE FOLK SONG

Dip and feather your paddles while you sing.

1. A - far up the riv - er, We pad - dle our ca - noe, ___ We dip and we feath - er, To slip through the wa - ters blue. ___ We dip, dip, to - geth - er, In rhythm that's true and strong, ___ A - far up the riv - er, We smooth - ly glide 'a - long. ___

2. A - way up the riv - er, We smooth - ly glide a - long, ___ We dip and we feath - er, And sing a ca - noe - ing song. ___ What mat - ters the weath - er? Our rhythm is strong and true, ___ A - way up the riv - er, We pad - dle our ca - noe. ___

MOCCASINED FEET

Where we walk to school each day
Indian children used to play—
All about our native land,
Where the shops and houses stand

And the trees were very tall,
And there were no streets at all,

Not a church and not a steeple—
Only wood and Indian people.

Only wigwams on the ground
And at night bears prowling round—
What a different place today
Where we live and work and play!
—ANNETTE WYNNE

Reprinted by permission of the publishers, J. B. Lippincott Company, from FOR DAYS AND DAYS, by Annette Wynne. Copyright 1947 by Annette Wynne.

The Peace Pipe

Use piano or tom-tom
for introduction and throughout:

ENGLISH WORDS BY LISBETH E. RAWSKI
CHIPPEWA INDIAN SONG

1. The flames are bright, broth-er,
2. For-get war dance, broth-er,

Sit with me to-night, broth-er,
Put a-way your lance, broth-er,

Let us join to-geth-er, Smoke the sa-cred pipe of peace.
Let us join to-geth-er, Smoke the sa-cred pipe of peace.

Come, let us smoke the sa-cred pipe of peace.

87

Butterflies, butterflies,
Now fly away to the blossoms,
Fly blue-wing,
Fly yellow-wing,
Now fly away to the blossoms,
Fly red-wing,
Fly white-wing,
Now fly away to the blossoms,
Butterflies, away!
Butterflies, butterflies,
Now fly away to the blossoms,
Butterflies, away!
—TRANSLATED BY NATALIE CURTIS
FROM THE LAGUNA INDIANS

My Corn Is Now Stretching Out Its Hands

ENGLISH WORDS BY RALPH HESS
PAPAGO INDIAN SONG

Play this song on the black keys of the piano.

My corn is now stretch - ing out its hands,

Now the corn is sing - ing to the sun.

In the des - ert breeze is sing - ing to the sun.

West wind sings; corn leaf sings.____

Use rain rattles for introduction and throughout:

Play this pattern on bells or piano:

Breezes Are Blowing

LUISENO INDIAN RAIN CHANT

Breez- es are blow - ing, Blow-ing clouds of wa - ter;

Breez- es are blow - ing, Blow-ing clouds of wa - ter;

On my face, rain - ing, Rain-ing from the o - cean;

Breez- es are blow - ing, Blow-ing clouds of wa - ter.

Hear Mosquito Buzzing

OJIBWAY INDIAN SONG

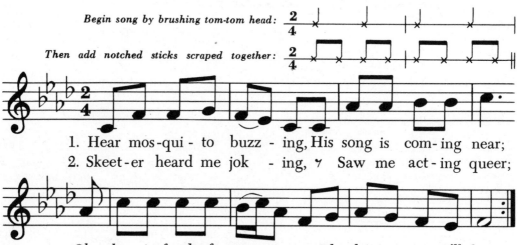

1. Hear mos-qui-to buzz-ing, His song is com-ing near;
2. Skeet-er heard me jok-ing, Saw me act-ing queer;

Oh, he is fond of gos-sip-ing, The lat-est news I'll hear.
Oh, then he went and buzzed a tale In-to my sweet-heart's ear.

3. Skeeter made his story strong,
Buzzed it loud and clear;
So when I went to call on her,
She boxed me on the ear.

Lullaby

OJIBWAY INDIAN SONG

Hush, lit-tle babe, go to sleep, lit-tle one;

Hush-a-bye, ba-by, don't cry____ I pray,

Or the great Na-ked Bear will come and take you a-way.

FLINTLOCKS AND SPINNING WHEELS

By the Fireside

On a little green knoll
At the edge of the wood
My great great grandmother's
First house stood.

The house was of logs,
My grandmother said,
With one big room
And a lean-to shed.

The logs were cut
And the house was raised
By pioneer men
In olden days.

I like to hear
My grandmother tell
How they built the fireplace
And dug the well.

They split the shingles;
They filled each chink;
It's a house of which
I like to think.

Forever and ever
I wish I could
Live in a house
At the edge of the wood.
　　　　　—JAMES S. TIPPETT

Dark Green Shawl

FOLK SONG FROM GEORGIA

This la - dy, she wears a dark green shawl,

A dark green shawl, a dark green shawl;

This la - dy, she wears a dark green shawl,

I love her to my heart.

Spinning Wheel

WORDS BY FRANCES B. WOOD
FLEMISH FOLK TUNE

*Make the sound of the spinning wheel
on the piano while you sing:*

1. All day I sit a - spin - ning,

A - spin - ning lin - en flax so fine,

All day I sit a - spin - ning,
No thread so white as mine.
And as my wheel spins round and round,
It makes a bus - y whir - ring sound.
All day I sit a - spin - ning,
A - spin - ning lin - en fine.

2. And as I spin I'm singing,
A-singing songs so sweet and gay,
And as I sit I'm singing
To pass the time away.
The bonny thread I swiftly wind,
No finer flax you'll ever find.
And as I spin I'm singing,
A-singing all the day.

Billy Boy

ENGLISH FOLK SONG

1. Oh,— where have you been, Bil-ly Boy, Bil-ly Boy,
2. Did she bid you to come in, Bil-ly Boy, Bil-ly Boy,

Oh,— where have you been, charm-ing Bil-ly?   I have
Did she bid you to come in, charm-ing Bil-ly?   Yes, she

been to seek a wife, She's the joy— of my life,
bid me to come in; There's a dim-ple in her chin,

She's a young thing and can-not leave her moth-er.——
She's a young thing and can-not leave her moth-er.——

3. Did she give you a chair, Billy Boy, Billy Boy?
    Yes, she gave me a chair, but there was no bottom there,

4. Can she make a cherry pie, Billy Boy, Billy Boy?
    She can make a cherry pie, quick as a cat can wink her eye,

5. Can she cook and can she spin, Billy Boy, Billy Boy?
    She can cook and she can spin, she can do most anything,

6. How old is she, Billy Boy, Billy Boy?
    Three times six and four times seven, twenty-eight and eleven,

Draw a Pail of Water

ENGLISH SINGING GAME

Draw a pail of wa - ter

For my la - dy's daugh - ter;

My fa - ther's a king and my moth - er's a queen;

My two lit - tle sis - ters are dressed in green.

One may rush, Two may rush;

Hur - ry up now, pop un - der.

Tam o' the Linn

IRISH STREET BALLAD

1. Tam o' the Linn had no breech-es to wear,
2. Tam o' the Linn had no shirt to his back,

He got an old sheep-skin to make him a pair;
He went to a neigh-bor's and bor-rowed a sack;

With the flesh-y side out and the
Then he puck-ered the meal bag in

wool-ly side in, "They'll be pleas-ant and
un-der his chin, "Sure, they'll take them for

cool," ____ says Tam o' the Linn.
ruf-fles," says Tam o' the Linn.

3. Tam o' the Linn was hard up for a coat,
So he borrowed the skin of a neighbor's goat;
With the horns sticking out from his pockets, and then,
"Sure, they'll take them for pistols,"
Says Tam o' the Linn.

4. Tam o' the Linn had no hat to put on,
   So he got an old beaver to make him a one;
   There was none of the crown left and less
         of the brim,
   "Sure there's fine ventilation,"
   Says Tam o' the Linn.

5. Tam o' the Linn had no shoes for his toes,
   He hopped in two crab-shells to serve him
         for those;
   Then he split up two oysters that matched
         like a twin,
   "Sure they'll shine out like buckles,"
   Says Tam o' the Linn.

6. Tam o' the Linn had no watch to put on,
   So he scooped out a turnip to make him
         a one;
   Then he placed a young cricket in under
         the skin,
   "Sure they'll think it is ticking,"
   Says Tam o' the Linn.

7. Tam o' the Linn to his house had no door,
   He'd the sky for a roof, and the bog for
         a floor;
   He'd a way to jump out, and a way to
         swim in,
   " 'Tis a fine place to live,"
   Says Tam o' the Linn.

The Quaker's Wife

OLD NURSERY SONG

The Quak - er's wife sat down to bake

With all ____ her bairns a - bout her.

She made them all a sug - ar cake,

And the mill - er he wants his mout - er.

Sug - ar and spice and all things nice,

And all things ver - y good in it, ____

And then the Quak - er sat down to play

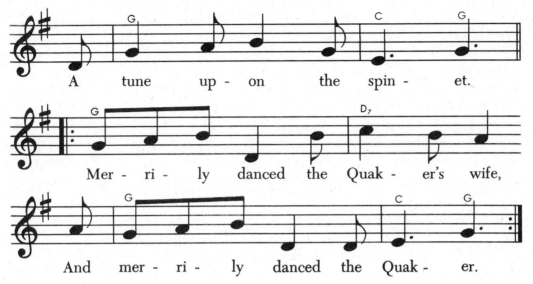

A tune up - on the spin - et.

Mer - ri - ly danced the Quak - er's wife,

And mer - ri - ly danced the Quak - er.

"Mouter" (moo-ter) is a miller's fee for grinding flour.
"Bairns" (bearns) is the Scottish word for children.

Minuet in F

WOLFGANG AMADEUS MOZART

The Riddle Song

FOLK SONG FROM KENTUCKY

1. I gave my love a cher-ry with-out a stone;

I gave my love a chick-en with-out a bone;

I gave my love a ring___ that has no end;

I gave my love a ba-by with no cry-in'.

2. How can there be a cherry without a stone?
   How can there be a chicken without a bone?
   How can there be a ring that has no end?
   How can there be a baby with no cryin'?

3. A cherry, when it's blooming, it has no stone;
   A chicken, when it's pippin', it has no bone;
   A ring when it's rolling, it has no end;
   A baby when it's sleeping, there's no cryin'.

100

All the Pretty Little Horses

FOLK SONG FROM SOUTHERN UNITED STATES

Melody bells begin this song and play this tune each time it is sung in song:

Hush-a - by, don't you cry,   Go to sleep-y, lit- tle ba - by.

When you wake, you shall have   All the pret-ty lit- tle hor - ses:

Blacks and bays, dap - ples and   grays,

Coach and six - a   lit - tle   hor - ses.

Hush- a - by, don't you cry,   Go to sleep-y, lit-tle ba - by.

101

Can You Tell Me?

FOLK SONG FROM PENNSYLVANIA

1. {Can you tell me how the farm - er, Can you
   {Oh, it's this way that the farm - er, Oh, it's

   tell me how the farm - er, Can you tell me
   this way that the farm - er, Oh, it's this way

   how the farm - er Plows his fields in the spring-time?
   that the farm - er Plows his fields in the spring-time,

   Can you tell me how the farm - er
   Oh, it's this way that the farm - er

   Plows his fields in the spring?
   Plows his fields in the spring.

2. Can you tell me how the farmer
   Sows his barley, his barley?
   Can you tell me how the farmer
   Sows his barley and oats?
   Oh, it's this way, etc.

3. Can you tell me how the farmer
   Cuts his barley and oats?

4. Can you tell me how he threshes
   His barley and oats?

102

A Churning Lilt

FOLK SONG FROM THE BRITISH ISLES

Play on piano before and throughout song:

1. Oh, Mar - y had a churn - ing
2. Would but - ter but come quick - ly,

A - down ___ by the wick, ___
Full blithe were we, I wist, ___

Sweet milk she would be turn - ing All in - to
With but - ter to the el - bow, But-ter - milk up

but - ter thick. }
to the wrist. } Quick, come but - ter, quick! But - ter -

milk and swe[et] but - ter, Quick, come but - ter, quick!

In Scottish dialect, a "wick" is a [dair]y house. "I wist" is "I know."

103

Hold On

AMERICAN FOLK SONG

d min.

1. When you plow, don't lose your track,—

d min.   A₇   d min.

Can't plow straight and keep a-look - ing back.—

d min.

Keep your hand on that plow,—

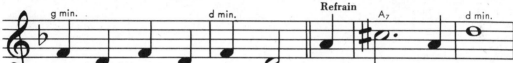

Hold on, hold on, hold on. Hold on, hold on,

Bet - ter keep your hand right on ____ that plow, ____

Hold on, hold on, hold on.

2. If you want to get to heaven, I'll tell you how,
   Keep your hand right on that plow.

3. Keep on plowing and don't you tire,
   Ev'ry row goes higher and higher.

4. If that plow stays in your hand,
   Head you straight for the promised land.

Down the Meadow

ENGLISH FOLK SONG

2. Be five little, be six little, we'll all go down the meadow;
Be seven little, be eight little, we'll all go down the meadow;
Be eight, be seven, be six, be five, be four, be three, be two, be one,
We'll have no more.
Hay me hay, carry me hay,
We'll all go down the meadow.

Add as many numbers as you like between °
and ° and then finish song.

Mary, Molly and I

WORDS BY JAMES SLOCUM
OLD ENGLISH TUNE

Finger cymbals twinkle:

1. Eve - ning light on   the pas - ture land,

Twin - kling,   twin - kling.

Down   we   go with our pails   in   hand,

Mar - y, Mol - ly and I.

2. Cowbells ringing a
     sleepy chime,
   Tinkling, tinkling.
   While we call o'er the
     meadow thyme,
   Mary, Molly, and I.

3. Sweet and warm is the milk
     we take,
   Every morning.
   When the daylight begins
     to break.
   Mary, Molly, and I.

Of a Tailor and a Bear

EDWARD MACDOWELL

I The Tailor is busily stitching

II when—The Bear pushes open his door

III Hoping to avoid trouble,
the Tailor tunes his fiddle

IV The Bear decides to be friendly and dances to the music

Play this introduction on a melody instrument:

Ollie in the Forest

ENGLISH WORDS BY KATE COX GODDARD
SWEDISH FOLK SONG

1. Ol - lie's a - lone in the for - est brown;
2. "Gruff, ruff ruff ruff," What is that, what is that?

Flow'rs look - ing up and trees look - ing down,
"Gruff, ruff ruff ruff," Not a dog, not a cat!

Brook - let a - laugh - ing to see Ol - lie play,
No, it's a bear with long shag - gy hair!

Birds, sing - ing clear, make the brown for - est gay.
"Come let us play, Mis - ter Bear, Mis - ter Bear."

3. Pat, pat-pat-pat! Ollie pats his head,
Bear looks at Ollie, hopes he'll be fed;
Bear eats some berries and looks all around,
Finding the ones Ollie spilled on the ground.

4. "Ollie, it's Mother, where have you been?"
Bear looks at Mother and runs for his den!
"Why, Mother, why did you scare him away?
Please ask the bear to come back here and play."

109

Mr. Raccoon

AMERICAN FOLK SONG

Refrain / Rhythm Sticks

Un - cle Reu-ben's rac - coon is gone, chick-a-chick,

Is gone, chick-a-chick, is gone, chick-a-chick,

Un - cle Reu-ben's rac - coon is gone, chick-a-chick,

End here

And left him there be - hind.

Verse

1. Rac - coon run - ning through the grass,
2. Pos - sum up a 'sim - mon tree,

Mis - ter Rac - coon, where you bound?
Mis - ter Rac - coon on the ground.

"Have no time to waste an - y words,
Rac - coon says, "Mister Pos - sum,___ please

Go back to the beginning

Mis - ter Pos - sum's com - ing down."
To ___ shake one 'sim - mon down."

Caught a Rabbit

KENTUCKY FOLK SONG
COLLECTED BY JEAN THOMAS, THE "TRAIPSIN' WOMAN"

Choose a child to sing the first part of each line.
The class sings the last part of each line.

Rab - bit run on the fro- zen ground! Who told you so?

Rab - bit run on the fro- zen ground! How do you know?

I caught a rab - bit, uh - huh!

I caught a rab - bit, uh - huh!

I caught a rab - bit, uh - huh!

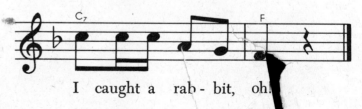

I caught a rab - bit, oh!

112

The Frog

PUERTO RICAN FOLK SONG

Play this song on melody flute.
Play finger cymbals or triangle on the last two lines.
Make up an accompaniment with rhythm instruments.

Lit - tle frog sings a lul - la - by soft - ly,
(*El   co - qui*)

I   can   hear   lit - tle   frog   all   night   long;
(*el   co - qui*)

Though I   fall   fast   a - sleep when   it's   bed - time,

In   my dreams comes his   sweet   lit - tle   song:

Co - kee!   Co - kee!   Co - kee - kee - kee - kee!

Co - kee!   Co - kee!   Co - kee - kee - kee - kee!

Coqui is pronounced koh-kee.

The Fox

ENGLISH FOLK SONG

1. The fox went out on a chil - ly night,
2. He ran till he came to a great big bin,

And ___ prayed for the moon for to give him light,
Where the ducks and the geese were ___ put there - in.

For he'd man - y a mile to go that night
"A ___ cou - ple of you will grease my chin

A - fore he reached the town - O, town - O town - O. He'd
A - fore I leave this town - O, town - O, town - O. A

man - y a mile to go that night a -
cou - ple of you will grease my chin a -

fore he reached the town - O. ___
fore I leave this town - O. ___

3. He grabbed the **gray goose** by the neck,
   Threw a duck across his back.
   He didn't mind their quack, quack, quack,
       And their legs all dangling down-O.

4. Then old Mother Flipper-Flopper jumped out of bed,
   Out of the window she cocked her head,
   Crying, "John! John! The gray goose is gone
       And the fox is on the town-O!"

5. Then John, he went to the top of the hill,
   Blew his horn both loud and shrill;
   The fox, he said, "I better flee with my kill
       Or they'll soon be on my trail-O."

6. He ran till he came to his cozy den,
   There were the little ones, eight, nine, ten.
   They said, "Daddy, better go back again,
       'Cause it must be a mighty fine town-O."

7. Then the fox and his wife, without any strife,
   Cut up the goose with a fork and knife;
   They never had such a supper in their life,
       And the little ones chewed on the bones-O.

The Mexican Woodpecker

WORDS AND MUSIC BY RALPH MARTUCCI

Two woodpeckers talk to each other before the song begins:

A Mex - i - can wood - peck - er high in a tree,

Went chick - chick - a - chick - a - chick all the day,

(clap - clap) He got so am - bi - tious he

wore off his beak, Now you can hear him say,___

"Oh, my beak, (clap - clap - clap) Oh, my beak, (clap - clap - clap)

What a sad day when I lost it!___

Hear me cry, *(clap-clap-clap)* Hear me sigh, *(clap-clap-clap)*

What a sor - ry sight to see, Poor me!"

Bird Songs

WORDS BY ELEANOR GRAHAM VANCE
MUSIC BY FRANCINE COCKENPOT

1. O - ho, _____ lis - ten to red - birds sing - ing their
2. O - ho, _____ sand - pip - er, run, O sand - pip - er,

song so wild and sweet; O - ho, _____ red - birds in
dance be - side the sea; O - ho, _____ sand - pip - er,

old mag - no - lia tree; O - ho, _____ lis - ten to
come and dance with me; O - ho, _____ sand - pip - er,

red - birds sing - ing their song so wild and sweet.
run, O sand - pip - er, dance be - side the sea.

Shoo, Fly, Don't Bother Me

AMERICAN SINGING GAME
FROM CIVIL WAR PERIOD

Shoo, fly, don't both - er me,

Shoo, fly, don't both - er me,

Shoo, fly, don't both - er me,

For I be - long to some - bod - y.

Verse

I feel, I feel, I feel,

I feel like a morn - ing star,

Fiddlin' Tunes

I feel, I feel, I feel, I feel,

I feel like a morn - ing star.

So Shoo, fly, don't both - er me,

Shoo, fly, don't both - er me,

Shoo, fly, don't both - er me,

For I be - long to some-bod - y.

Lady in the Pond

SOUTHERN FOLK GAME SONG
COLLECTED BY JOHN W. WORK

1. La - dy in the pond, She won't come a - long,___
2. Call___ your___ love, She won't come a - long,___

La - dy in the pond,___ She won't come a - long;___
Call___ your___ love, ___ She won't come a - long, ___

La - dy in the pond, She won't come a - long,___
Call___ your___ love, She won't come a - long,___

She'll be there soon in the morn - ing.
She'll be there soon in the morn - ing.

3. Swing your love,
   She won't come along,
   Swing your love,
   She won't come along,
   Swing your love,
   She won't come along,
   She'll be there soon in the morning.

The Old Brass Wagon

AMERICAN PLAY-PARTY GAME

1. Cir - cle to the left, the Old Brass Wag - on;

Cir - cle to the left, the Old Brass Wag - on;

Cir - cle to the left, the Old Brass Wag - on;

You're the one, my dar - ling.

2. Circle to the right, the Old Brass Wagon;

3. Swing, oh swing, the Old Brass Wagon;

4. Promenade right, the Old Brass Wagon;

5. Walk it up and down, the Old Brass Wagon;

6. Break and swing, the Old Brass Wagon;

Pop Goes the Weasel

AMERICAN SQUARE DANCE TUNE

1. A pen - ny for a spool___ of thread, A
2. Po - ta - toes for an I - rish - man's taste, A

pen - ny for a nee - dle, That's the way the
doc - tor for the mea - sles, A fid - dler al - ways

mon - ey goes, Pop goes the wea - sel!
for___ a dance, or Pop goes the wea - sel! Blood

All a - round the cob - bler's bench The
pud - ding for a Dutch - man's meal, A

mon - key chased the wea - sel, The mon - key thought 'twas
work - man for a chis - el, The tune that ev - 'ry -

all in fun, } Pop goes the wea - sel!
bod - y sings is }

122

3. From round about the countrymen's barn,
   The mice begin to mizzle;
   For when they poke their noses out,
   Pop goes the weasel!
   The painter works with ladder and brush,
   The artist with the easel,
   The fiddler always snaps the string at
   Pop goes the weasel!

Paper of Pins

AMERICAN FOLK SONG

Choose a boy and a girl to act out this story.

(He) 1. I'll give to you this pa-per of pins, And
(She) 2. No, I'll not ac-cept your pa-per of pins, If

that's the way our love a-gins, If you will
that's the way your love a-gins, And I'll not

mar-ry me, me, me, If you will mar-ry me. __
mar-ry you, you, you, And I'll not mar-ry you. __

3. *(He)* I'll give to you this dress of red,
All stitched around with golden thread,
If you will marry me, me, me,
If you will marry me.

4. *(She)* No, I'll not accept your dress of red,
All stitched around with golden thread,
And I'll not marry you, you, you,
And I'll not marry you.

5. *(He)* I'll give to you this old big horse,
That paced these hills from cross to cross,

6. *(She)* No, I'll not accept your old big horse,
That paced these hills from cross to cross,

7. *(He)* I'll give to you a house and land,
A herd of cattle, a good hired hand,

124

8. *(She)* No, I'll not accept your house and land,
And herd of cattle and good hired hand,

9. *(He)* I'll give to you my hand and my heart,
That we might marry and never part,

10. *(She)* Yes, I'll accept your hand and your heart,
That we might marry and never part,
And I will marry you, you, you,
And I will marry you.

The Needle's Eye

AMERICAN SINGING GAME

Play these notes on the bells:

Oh, the nee - dle's eye that doth sup - ply the

thread that runs so tru - ly; There's man - y a

lass did I let pass Be - cause I want - ed you.___
lad that I left sad Be - cause I want - ed you. ___

You, you, you,___ you, you, you,___There's man-y a

lass did I let pass Be -cause I want - ed you.___
lad that I left sad Be -cause I want - ed you.___

Hoofs and Wheels

Hop Up, My Ladies

AMERICAN FOLK SONG

1. Did you ev - er go to meet - ing, Un - cle

Joe, Un - cle Joe? Did you ev - er go to

meet - ing, Un - cle Joe? ___ Did you ev - er go to

meet - ing, Un - cle Joe, Un - cle Joe?

Don't mind the weath - er, so the wind don't blow.

2. Will your horse carry double, Uncle Joe, Uncle Joe?
   Don't mind the weather, so the wind don't blow.

Refrain

Hop up, my la - dies, three in a row,

Hop up, my la - dies, three in a row,

Hop up, my la - dies, three in a row,

Don't mind the weath - er,

so the wind don't blow.

.... horse a single-footer, Uncle Joe, Uncle Joe?
.... the weather, so the wind don't blow.

127

Yankee Doodle

WORDS AND TUNE TRADITIONAL

Make a parade out of this:

Clap or use coconut shells 2/4 ♪♪ ♪♪ *for a pony trot*

For marching use drum 2/4 ♩♩ | ♩ ♩ *and cymbals* 2/4 ♩ 𝄽 | ♩ 𝄽 |

1. Yan-kee Doo-dle came to town, Rid-ing on a po - ny;

Stuck a feath-er in his cap And called it Mac-a - ro - ni.

Refrain

Yan- kee Doo-dle keep it up, Yan- kee Doo-dle dan - dy,

Mind the mu- sic and the step And with the girls be hand - y.

2. Fath'r and I went down to camp,
Along with Captain Goodwin,
And there we saw the men and boys,
As thick as hasty pudding.

3. There was Captain Wash___ton,
Upon a slapping stal___
A-giving orders to his___
I guess there was a m___

128

She'll Be Comin' Round the Mountain

SOUTHERN MOUNTAIN SONG

Use coconut shells or tone blocks for hoof beats.

1. She'll be com - in' round the moun-tain when she comes, ___
2. She'll be driv - in' six white hor - ses when she comes, ___

She'll be com - in' round the moun-tain when she comes, ___
She'll be driv - in' six white hor - ses when she comes, ___

She'll be com - in' round the moun - tain,
She'll be driv - in' six white hor - ses,

She'll be com - in' round the moun - tain,
She'll be driv - in' six white hor - ses,

She'll be com - in' round the moun- tain when she comes. ___
She'll be driv - in' six white hor - ses when she comes. ___

3. Oh, we'll kill the old red rooster when she comes,

4. Oh, we'll all have chicken and dumplings when she comes,

5. Oh, we'll all go out to meet her when she comes,

Riding in the Buggy

FOLK SONG FROM SOUTHERN UNITED STATES

1. Rid - ing in the bug - gy, Miss Mar - y Jane,

Miss Mar - y Jane, Miss Mar - y Jane,

Rid - ing in the bug - gy, Miss Mar - y Jane,

I'm a long way from home.

Who moans for me? Who moans for me?

Who moans for me, my dar- ling? Who moans for me?

2. I've got a house in Baltimore,
In Baltimore,
In Baltimore,
I've got a house in Baltimore,
And it's full of chicken pie.

3. I've got a girl in Baltimore,
In Baltimore,
In Baltimore,
I've got a girl in Baltimore,
And she's three stories high.

131

Hot Corn

NEW YORK STREET CRY

Hot corn, ___ hot corn, ___ Here's your nice sweet corn,

All pip- ing ___ hot; Hot corn, ___ hot corn, ___

Here's your nice sweet corn, All pip -ing ___ hot; Hot corn, ___

hot corn, ___ Here's your nice sweet corn, All pip-ing ___ hot.

The Country Store

WORDS AND MUSIC BY EVELYN H. HUNT

1. In the coun - try store at the end of the street
2. At the coun - try store, there are can - dies ___ fine,

132

Ev - 'ry-bod - y gath - ers   to buy them-selves a   treat.
Pep-per-mint and lem - on,   7 cin - na - mon and lime,

Big   and   lit - tle,   thin   and   fat,
Jump - ing   ropes   and   col - ored   tops,

Jon - a - than,   Jen - nie,   Paul   and   Pat.
Lic - o - rice   sticks   and   choc - 'late   drops.

Refrain
At   the coun - try   store   we have plen - ty   of   fun,

Go   there ev - 'ry   week   when   work   is   done,

We   spend our   mon - ey,   And   wish we   had some more,

To   spend   at   the coun - try   store.

The Swapping Song

ENGLISH FOLK SONG

1. Oh, when I was a lit - tle boy, I

lived by my - self,___ And all the bread and

cheese I had, I kept on a shelf.___

Refrain

To my wing wong wad - dle, to my

Jack straw strad - dle, To my John fair

fad - dle, to my long - ways home.

134

2. The rats and the mice, they led me such
      a life,
   I had to go to London to get me a wife.

3. The roads were so slick and the lanes were so
      narrow,
   I had to bring her home in an old wheelbarrow.

4. My foot it slipped and I got a fall,
   And down came my wheelbarrow, wife
      and all.

5. I swapped my wheelbarrow, got me a
      horse,
   And then I rode from cross to cross.

6. I swapped my horse and I got me a mare,
   And then I rode from fair to fair.

7. I swapped my mare and I got me a cow,
   And in that trade I just learned how.

8. I swapped my cow and I got me a calf,
   And in that trade I just lost half.

9. I swapped my calf and I got me a sheep,
   And then I rode till I went to sleep.

10. I swapped my sheep and I got me a hen,
    For to lay me an egg every now and then.

11. I swapped my hen and I got me a rat,
    And I set it on the haystack to run
       the cat.

12. I swapped my rat and I got me a mole,
    And the blind old thing went straight to
       its hole.

I'm a Tinker

SLOVAK FOLK SONG

Play refrain on melody bells as an introduction:

"Old pans to mend, Old pans to mend!

Come one, come all! Old pans to mend!"

1. I'm a tink - er, I'm a good one,
2. I'm a tink - er, I'm a good one,

Tren - chin Coun - ty gave me birth;
Tink - er was, am, and shall be.

Mend - ing bro - ken pans and skil - lets,
See me walk - ing through the vil - lage,

On I wan - der through the earth.
Sing - ing loud and mer - ri - ly.

3. See me walking through the village,
   Ev'ryone is glad I've come.
   "Stop, dear tinker!" hear them calling,
   "I've a broken pan at home."

The Miller Boy

AMERICAN SINGING GAME

1. Hap-py is the mill-er boy who lives by the mill, The mill turns a-round with a right good will; One hand on the hop-per and the oth-er on the sack, Ev-'ry time the wheel turns, turn right back.

2. Hap-py is the mill-er boy who lives by the mill, The mill turns a-round with a right good will; One hand on the hop-per and the oth-er on the slab, Ev-'ry time the wheel turns, grab, boys, grab.

The Blacksmith

ENGLISH FOLK SONG

1. Here's a song for the jol - ly black - smith, The
2. Here's a song for the jol - ly black - smith, The

best of all fel - lows, Who works at his
strong - est of all, _____ Who makes his big

an - vil While the boy blows the bel - lows.
ham - mer To _____ rise and to fall. _____

Refrain

Twan - ky - dil - lo, twan - ky - dil - lo, twan - ky -

dil - lo, dil - lo, dil - lo, dil - lo, A roar - ing

pair of bag - pipes made of the green wil - low.

3. Here's a song for the jolly blacksmith,
   He's clever, indeed.
   He shapes every horseshoe
   To a fit for each steed.

4. Here's a song for the jolly blacksmith,
   He's handy, besides,
   He rims wheels for wagons,
   So that we can have rides.

HAPPY DAYS

The Seasons

WORDS BY EVELYN H. HUNT
BRETON FOLK MELODY

1. The fall is here, the win-ter's near, Farm-ers are
2. The spring is here, the sum-mer's near, Flow-ers are

gath-er-ing the har-vest, The leaves are bright, the
bloom-ing in the mead-ow, The birds all sing, they

pump-kin's ripe, Sing fa la la, Sing fa la lay,
know 'tis spring, Sing fa la la, Sing fa la lay,

Sing fa la la la la la lay, lay.
Sing fa la la la la la lay, lay.

The leaves are bright, the pump-kin's ripe, Sing fa la la,
The birds all sing, they know 'tis spring, Sing fa la la,

140

Sing fa la lay, Sing fa la la la la la
Sing fa la lay, Sing fa la la la la la

lay, lay. The fall is here, the win - ter's near,
lay, lay. The spring is here, the sum - mer's near,

Farm - ers are gath - er - ing the har - vest.
Flow - ers are bloom - ing in the mead - ow.

Stars

WORDS AND MUSIC BY ERNEST GOLD

Stars like jew-els in the night, Blue stars, white stars;

Stars like sparks of sil-ver light, Small stars, big stars;

Shoot-ing stars like birds in flight, Bright stars, dim stars.

Clouds

POEM BY CHRISTINA ROSSETTI
MUSIC BY HOAGY CARMICHAEL

White sheep, white sheep, High on a wind-y hill,

When the wind stops, You all stand still;

But when the wind blows, You walk a-way slow.

Oh, white sheep, white sheep, Where do you go?

Moon Cradle

POEM BY PADRAIC COLUM
MUSIC BY MILTON KAYE

Play an octave higher on the piano before
singing and continue throughout song:

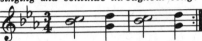

The moon cra - dle's rock - ing, rock - ing, ____

Where a cloud and a cloud goes by; ____

Si - lent - ly rock - ing and rock - ing, ____

The moon cra - dle out in the sky. ____

Waltz

FRANZ SCHUBERT

On stormy days when the wind is high
Tall trees are brooms sweeping the sky.
They swish their branches in buckets of rain
And swash and sweep it clean again.
—DOROTHY ALDIS

When the music dips low, swish brooms in buckets of rain. When the music soars, sweep the sky.

144

Halloween

WORDS BY HARRY BEHN
MUSIC BY MILTON KAYE

To - night is the night when dead leaves fly

Like witch - es on switch - es a - cross the sky.

When elf and sprite flit through the night on a

moon - y sheen, It's Hal - low- een.____

Birthday Song

CAMP SONG

Oh, {Su - sie Smith}
   {John - ny Jones} we sing - a - ling - a - ling

With all our hearts to you,

Melody Bells

We hope there'll be some - thing - a - ling - a - ling

That we can do for you;

Melody Bells

In au - tumn, win - ter, spring - a - ling - a - ling,

And all the whole year through,

Melody Bells

We'll ring - a - ling - a - ling, And sing - a - ling - a - ling,

And ching - a - ling - a - ling for you. _____

Melody Bells

Mince Pie or Pudding

SHAKER WELCOME SONG

Play this introduction on a melody instrument:

Wel - come, here, wel - come here,

All be a - live and be of good cheer,

I've got a pie all baked com - plete, _____

Pud - ding, too, that's ver - y sweet.

We Thank Thee

POEM BY RALPH WALDO EMERSON
MUSIC BY ARTHUR C. EDWARDS

1. For flowers that bloom a - bout our feet,
2. For blue of stream and blue of sky,

For ten - der grass, so fresh, so sweet,
For pleas - ant shade of branch - es high,

For song of bird and hum of bee,
For fra - grant air and cool - ing breeze,

For all things fair we hear or see,
For beau - ty of the bloom - ing trees,

Fa - ther in Heav - en, we thank Thee.

Swing the Shining Sickle

WORDS BY ALICE C. D. RILEY
MUSIC BY JESSIE L. GAYNOR

1. Swing the shin - ing sick - le, Cut the rip-ened grain,
2. Loud - ly blows the north-wind Through the shiv-'ring trees,

Flash it in the sun - light, Swing it once a - gain.
Bare are all the branch - es, Fall - en all the leaves.

Tie the gold- en grain- heads In - to shin - ing sheaves,
Gath- ered is the har - vest For an - oth- er year,

Beau - ti - ful their col - ors As the au - tumn leaves.
Now our day of glad - ness, Thanks-giving Day is here.

Eight Nights of Hanukah

WORDS BY FREDA PRENSKY
HEBREW FOLK TUNE

Flick- er, lit - tle can - dles, flick- er bright for Ha - nu- kah,

Flick- er lit - tle can - dles, all eight nights of Ha - nu- kah.

Lit - tle tops are spin-ning round and round on Ha - nu- kah,

Lit - tle tops are spin - ning, Ha - nu - kah is here.

Bells

WORDS BY W. SEDGWICK
FOLK SONG ARRANGED BY DESMOND MacMAHON

*Melody bells or piano peal out Christmas
chimes, to begin song:*

Play encircled notes on the piano, verses 1 and 2; on melody bells, verse 3.

1. A - swing - ing, a - ring - ing, The bells at

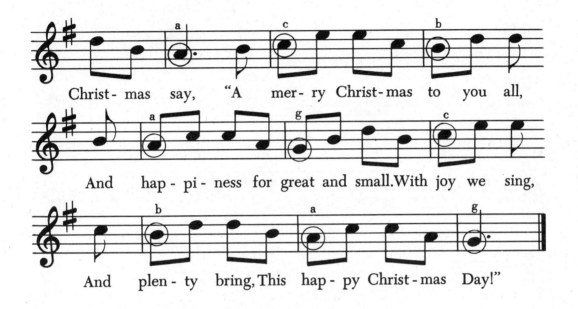

Christ-mas say, "A mer-ry Christ-mas to you all,

And hap-pi-ness for great and small. With joy we sing,

And plen-ty bring, This hap-py Christ-mas Day!"

2. A-clanging, a-banging,
   The bells each morning say,
   "Get out of bed, you sleepyhead!
   The sun will soon be overhead,
   You must not doze,
   Put on your clothes,
   It's time to say, 'Good-day.'"

3. How lowly and slowly
   The bells, with evening light,
   Say, "Now's the time for sleeping,
   And children all are creeping
   Away upstairs,
   To say their prayers,
   It's time to say, 'Good-night.'"

Carol of the Birds

CZECH CAROL

1. From out of a wood did a cuck-oo fly, Cuck-oo,

He came to a man-ger with joy-ful cry, Cuck-oo;

He hopped, he curt-sied, 'round he flew, And loud his

ju - bi - la - tion grew, Cuck-oo, cuck-oo, cuck-oo.____

2. A pigeon flew over to Galilee, Ver-croo,
   He strutted and cooed and was full of glee, Ver-croo;
   And showed with jewelled wings unfurled,
   His joy that Christ was in the world,
   Ver-croo, ver-croo, ver-croo.

3. A dove settled down upon Nazareth, Tsu-croo,
   And tenderly chanted with all his breath, Tsu-croo;
   "O you," he cooed, "so good and true,
   My beauty do I give to you,
   Tsu-croo, tsu-croo, tsu-croo."

O Come, Little Children

ENGLISH VERSION ANONYMOUS
MELODY BY J. SCHULZ

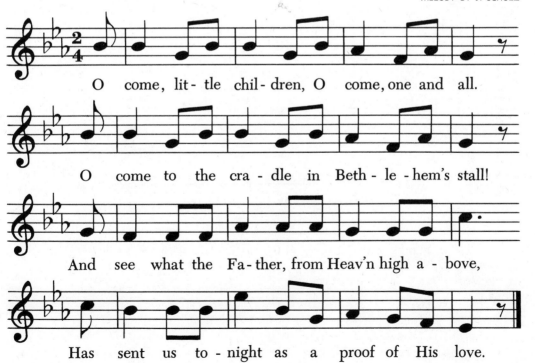

O come, lit-tle chil-dren, O come, one and all.

O come to the cra-dle in Beth-le-hem's stall!

And see what the Fa-ther, from Heav'n high a-bove,

Has sent us to-night as a proof of His love.

It Came upon a Midnight Clear

WORDS BY EDMUND H. SEARS
MUSIC BY RICHARD S. WILLIS

1. It came up - on ___ the mid - night clear,
2. Still thro' the clo - ven skies they come,

That glo - rious song ___ of old, ___ From an - gels bend - ing
With peace - ful wings ___ un - furled; ___ And still their heav - en - ly

near the earth, To touch their harps ___ of gold: ___
mu - sic floats O'er all the wea - ry world: ___

"Peace on the earth, ___ good will to men
A - bove its sad ___ and low - ly plains

From heav - en's all - gra - cious King." ___ The world in sol - emn
They bend ___ on hov - 'ring wing, ___ And ev - er o'er ___ its

still - ness lay To hear the an - gels sing. ___
Ba - bel sounds The bless - ed an - gels sing. ___

O Come, All Ye Faithful

WORDS BY FREDERICK OAKELEY
MUSIC BY J. READING

1. O come, all ye faith - ful, Joy - ful and tri -
2. Sing, choirs of an - gels, Sing in ex - ul -

um - phant, O come ye, O come___ ye to
ta - tion, O sing, all ye cit - i - zens of

Beth - le - hem; Come and be - hold Him,
Heav'n___ a - bove! Glo - ry to God___

Refrain

Born the King of An - gels.
in___ the___ high - est. O come let us a -

dore Him, O come let us a - dore Him, O

come let us a - dore Him,___ Christ ___ the Lord.

Piñata

WORDS TRANSLATED BY NONA K. DUFFY
MEXICAN CHRISTMAS SONG

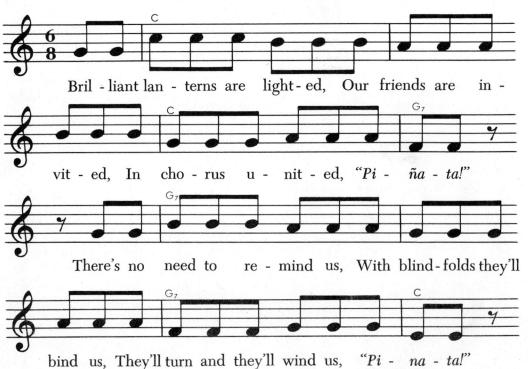

Bril - liant lan - terns are light - ed, Our friends are in -

vit - ed, In cho - rus u - nit - ed, "Pi - ña - ta!"

There's no need to re - mind us, With blind - folds they'll

bind us, They'll turn and they'll wind us, "Pi - na - ta!"

The *pi - ña - ta,* the *pi - ña - ta,* Holds the

can - dies for neigh-bors and cous - ins; We will

whack it, we will crack it, And the good-ies will

fall down in doz - ens. All the chil - dren will

scram - ble for can - dy, All the chil - dren will

scram - ble and shout; All the chil-dren will grab for a

cook - y and the oth- er good things that spill out.

Jingle Bells

WORDS AND MUSIC BY JAMES PIERPONT

1. Dash-ing through the snow In a one-horse o - pen sleigh,
2. Day or two a - go I— thought I'd take a ride

O'er the fields we go, Laugh-ing all the way;
And soon Miss Fan- ny Bright Was seat-ed by my side;

Bells on bob- tail ring, Mak-ing spir - its bright,
The horse was lean and lank, Mis-for-tune seemed his lot,

What fun it is to ride and sing A sleigh-ing song to -night!
He got in - to a drift-ed bank, And we, we got up- sot.

Jin - gle bells, jin - gle bells, jin - gle all the way!

Oh, what fun it is to ride in a one-horse o - pen sleigh!—

Jin - gle bells, jin - gle bells, jin - gle all the way!

Oh, what fun it is to ride in a one - horse o - pen sleigh!

I Saw Three Ships

ENGLISH CAROL

1. I saw three ships come sail - ing by,
2. And what d'you think was in them then,
3. Three pret - ty girls were in them then,

Sail - ing by, sail - ing by,
In ____ them then, in ____ them then,
In ____ them then, in ____ them then,

I saw three ships come sail - ing by,
And what d'you think was in them then,
Three pret - ty girls were in them then,

On Christ - mas Day in the morn - ing.

January and February

WORDS BY JANE B. WALTERS
GERMAN FOLK SONG

1. When Jan - u - ar - y days are here,
2. When Feb - ru - ar - y north wind blows,

The air is crisp, the sky is clear,
The hills and roads are heaped with snow,

Come join our out - door play;
Come join our in - door play;

Come with us, join our out - door play.
Come with us, join our in - door play.

For __ o'er the ice we're glid - ing,
Like __ lit - tle gob - lins hop - ping,

Or down the hill __ we're slid - ing,
The feather - y corn __ is pop - ping,

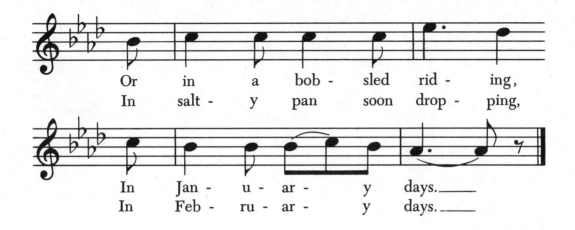

Or in a bob - sled rid - ing,
In salt - y pan soon drop - ping,

In Jan - u - ar - y days.____
In Feb - ru - ar - y days.____

America

WORDS BY SAMUEL FRANCIS SMITH
MUSIC BY HENRY CAREY

1. My coun - try! 'Tis of thee, Sweet land of lib - er - ty,
2. My na - tive coun - try, thee, Land of the no - ble free,
3. Our fa - thers' God, to Thee, Au - thor of lib - er - ty,

Of thee I sing; Land where my fa - thers died, Land of the
Thy name I love; I love thy rocks and rills, Thy woods and
To Thee we sing; Long may our land be bright With free - dom's

Pil - grims' pride, From ev - 'ry__ moun - tain side Let_ free - dom ring.
tem - pled hills, My heart__ with__ rap - ture thrills Like__ that a - bove.
ho - ly light; Pro - tect__ us __ by Thy might, Great God, our King.

Winter

POEM BY DOROTHY ALDIS
MUSIC BY MILTON KAYE

The street-cars are like frost-ed cakes

All cov-ered up with cold snow-flakes,

The hor-ses' hoofs scrunch in the street,

Their eye-lash-es are white with sleet,

And, ev-'ry-where, the peo-ple go

With fa-ces tick-led by the snow.

A Valentine

WORDS BY EVELYN H. HUNT
DUTCH FOLK TUNE

1. I sent my love a val - en - tine, val - en - tine,

val - en - tine, I sent my love a val - en - tine,

and {he she} will get it soon. **Refrain** Val - en - tine,

val - en - tine, sent my love a val - en - tine,

Val - en - tine, val - en - tine, {He She} will get it soon.

2. The valentine had hearts of lace,
Hearts of lace, hearts of lace,
The valentine had hearts of lace,
And he will get it soon.

3. It said to him, "Will you be mine,
You be mine, you be mine?"
It said to him, "Will you be mine?"
And he will get it soon.

America, the Beautiful

WORDS BY KATHERINE LEE BATES
MUSIC BY SAMUEL A. WARD

O beau - ti - ful for spa - cious skies, For

am - ber waves of grain, For pur - ple moun - tain

maj - es - ties A - bove the fruit - ed plain!

A - mer - i - ca! A - mer - i - ca! God

shed His grace on thee, And crown thy good with

broth - er - hood From sea to shin - ing sea!

Spring Carnival

POEM BY ROWENA B. BENNETT
MUSIC BY ARTHUR C. EDWARDS

Wind blows a bugle:

or

Rain beats a drum:

Melody Bells

1. The wind blew his bu - gle, The rain beat his drum;
2. The tu - lips all came in their dress - es of flame,

The sun, like a her - ald, cried so joy-ful - ly to come.
And a snow - drop was wear-ing there a flow-er in her hair.

Come to the car - ni - val of spring, of spring.
Dance at the car - ni - val of spring, of spring.

Listen to the Rain

WORDS AND MUSIC BY MILTON KAYE

Melody Bells

Lis - ten to the rain, On my win-dow pane,

Hear each drop go plop, Will it ev - er stop?

Plink, plank, plink, Plunk, plink, plunk.____

Hear the rain Sing on my win - dow pane.____

May Baskets

WORDS BY GRACE LANG
MUSIC BY H. G. NAGELI

1. When the first rob - ins sing in the tree - tops,

Then we know that Spring is sure - ly here,

And when we hear them sing - ing high up in the branch - es,

Hap - py, hap - py May Day must be here.

2. Come, let us look for earliest flowers,
   Yellow ones or red, or pink or blue,
   We'll gather them in fields and gather them in gardens,
   Purple violets and snow drops too.

3. This is the day we make pretty baskets,
   Fill them up with flowers, every one.
   To some one that we love, we give a little basket,
   Hang it on the big front door, then run!

Summer Day

WORDS BY MARGARET MARKS
SWISS FOLK SONG

*Dramatize the story. Imitate the sounds of the
busy bee, the fat bird, and the shiny fish.*

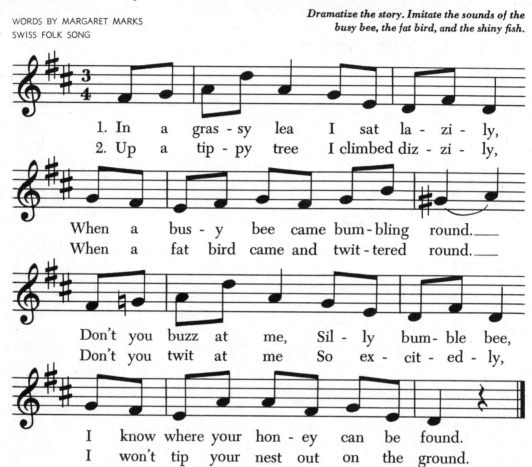

1. In a gras - sy lea I sat la - zi - ly,
2. Up a tip - py tree I climbed diz - zi - ly,

When a bus - y bee came bum - bling round.___
When a fat bird came and twit - tered round.___

Don't you buzz at me, Sil - ly bum - ble bee,
Don't you twit at me So ex - cit - ed - ly,

I know where your hon - ey can be found.
I won't tip your nest out on the ground.

3. In the briny sea
   I swam easily,
   When a shiny fish came swimming round.
   "Don't you swish at me
   Quite so fishily,
   I might catch you if you stay around."

Classified Index

169

Index to Instrumental Music

172